Introducing Community Care

Titles available in the
Working with People Series

Introducing Community Care

Peter Sharkey

Collins Educational
An Imprint of HarperCollins*Publishers*

Published by
Collins Educational Ltd
77–85 Fulham Palace Road
Hammersmith
London
W6 8JB

First Published 1995
Reprinted 1995

British Cataloguing in Publication Data is available from the British Library.

ISBN 0–00–3223337

Typeset by Harper Phototypesetters Limited, Northampton, England
Cover design by Wheeler and Porter
Printed in Great Britain by Scotprint, Musselburgh

Contents

To my mother and father.

Acknowledgements

The author would like to thank colleagues at the Liverpool John Moores University for help and comments, especially Beverley Burke, Simon Rahilly and John Mayhew. Kate Griffiths provided information on the Birmingham Community Care Special Action Project (Chapter 8). Cindy Sharkey made extensive and valuable comments on the whole text as did Patrick McNeill of HarperCollins and Louise Wilson, the editor.

The publisher and the author would also like to thank the following.

The Audit Commission for permission to reproduce an extract from *Making a Reality of Community Care* (1986).

British Deaf Association for permission to reproduce an extract from *Britain's Deaf Heritage* (Jackson, 1990).

CACI for permission to reproduce an illustration from *Managing the New NHS* (DoH, 1993d).

The Race Equality Unit for permission to reproduce an extract from *Review of the Report of the Inquiry into the Care and Treatment of Christopher Clunis: A Black Perspective* (Harris, 1994).

Crown copyright is reproduced with the permission of the Controller of Her Majesty's Stationery Office for extracts from *Care Management and Assessment: Practitioners' Guide*; *Carers: Research and Practice* (Twigg, 1992); *Committed to Quality*; *Community Care Agenda for Action* (Griffiths, 1988); *Community Care in the Next Decade and Beyond: Policy Guidance*; *Factors Influencing the Implementation of the Care Programme Approach* (North, Ritchie and Ward, 1993); *Mentally Incapacitated and other Vulnerable Adults Public Law Protection* (Law Commission, 1993); *No Longer Afraid: Practice Guidelines*; *Purchase of Service: Practice Guidance*; *The Report of the Inquiry into the Care and Treatment of Christopher Clunis* (Ritchie, Dick and Lingham, 1994).

Dispatches — *Relative Hell* was produced by Fulcum Productions for Channel Four Television Corporation.

Family Policy Studies Centre for permission to reproduce an extract from *The Family Today: Fact Sheet 1* (1991).

Gower Publishers for permission to reproduce an extract from *Care Management in Community Care* (Challis and Davies, 1986).

The King's Fund for permission to reproduce extracts from *Meeting the Challenge* (King's Fund Centre, 1991), *Checklist: Health and Race* (Gunaratnam, 1993) and *Bridging the Gap* (Hunter, 1988).

Lion Publishing for permission to reproduce an extract from *A New Deal for Social Welfare* (Holman, 1993).

Local Government Drugs Forum for permission to reproduce an extract from *Fast Track Assessment for People with Alcohol and Drug Problems* (LGDF, 1993).

London Voluntary Services Council for permission to reproduce an extract from *Who Really Cares?* (Phaure, 1991).

Macmillan Press Ltd for permission to reproduce extracts from *Feminist Perspective on Caring* (Graham, 1993); *Citizen Involvement* (Beresford. and Croft, 1993) and *Independent Lives* (Morris, 1993).

MIND for permission to reproduce an extract from *Policy on Black and Minority Ethnic People and Mental Health* (MIND, 1993).

The extract from *Nye Bevan Would Turn in His Grave* (Vousden, 1987) is reproduced by kind permission of Nursing Times where this article first appeared on August 12th 1987.

Pepar Publications for permission to reproduce an extract from *Vocational Qualifications in Care* (Harvey and Tisdal, 1992).

Routledge Publishers Ltd for permission to reproduce extracts from 'The Limits to Integration' (Szivos, 1992) in *Normalisation* (Brown and Smith, 1992).

The Royal Association for Disability and Rehabilitation (RADAR) for permission to reproduce an extract from *Carers at the Crossroads* (Simpson, 1991).

Runnymede Trust for permission to reproduce an extract from *A 'Race' Against Time* (Patel, 1990).

School for Advanced Urban Studies, University of Bristol for permission to reproduce extracts from *Brokerage in Action* (Harrison and Means, 1993) and *Working Better Together for Community Care* (Smith, 1993).

Social Policy Association for permission to reproduce extracts from *Somewhere Over the Rainbow: Universality and Diversity in Social Policy* (Williams, 1992) and *Social Policy Review* (Manning and Page, 1992).

Survivors Speak Out for permission to reproduce an extract from *Self-Advocacy Action Pack* (Survivors Speak Out, 1988).

UNISON for permission to reproduce extracts from *Guidelines for Empowering Users of Mental Health Services* (MIND, 1993).

Introduction

This book is an introduction to community care and to the considerable changes that took place in the early 1990s. It is a text suitable for anyone wanting a broad overview of these changes and the current arrangements for community care.

Community care is an important and fascinating area to study. It raises questions such as:

- How should we care for the most vulnerable members of our society?
- Who does the caring in our society and who should do the caring?
- How much care should the state provide and how much should the family provide?
- Should help go to carers or directly to disabled and older people who can then purchase their own care?
- Should social policy be based on values of self-interest or values of sharing?

These are among the issues which will be discussed in this book.

Chapter 1 gives the background to the legislative changes and details of the changes themselves. Chapter 2 attempts to answer the question 'Who are the carers?' in relation to both paid and unpaid carers. Chapter 3 looks at the ideas of normalisation, disability and social oppression, and the independent living movement. Chapter 4 considers race, anti-racism and community care. Care management and assessment are the main themes of Chapter 5. This is followed in Chapter 6 by a focus on abuse and harm within the context of community care. Contracts and quality assurance are the two themes of Chapter 7. The book concludes by looking at user empowerment in Chapter 8.

Professional training

The book will be a useful introductory text for any student of community care. It will be a helpful introduction for social care and health care workers engaged in their professional training. It will also be helpful for workers and students engaged in achieving Scottish or National Vocational Qualifications (S/NVQs) or General National Vocational Qualifications (GNVQs).

S/NVQs in Care

1992 saw the introduction of the 'National Occupational Standards for Care'. The Care S/NVQs are applicable for staff groups with job titles such as Nursing Auxiliary, Health Care Assistant, Health Care Support Worker, Physiotherapy Assistant, Occupational Therapy Aide, Care Assistant, Care Attendant and

Home Help. These are people working in settings such as day-care centres, health care support services, residential homes and community care projects.

S/NVQs in Care essentially assess workers' competence in the workplace. This attempt to integrate the awards across the health care field and the social care field recognises that there is a lot of similar work done no matter which field people are actually employed in.

This book will particularly help towards underpinning knowledge for the 'O' Unit of the National Occupational Standards, which contains the values and skills that are at the heart of care delivery. The title of this Value Base Unit is 'Promote Equality For All Individuals'. The five elements which make up the 'O' Unit are:

1 promote anti-discriminatory practice;
2 maintain the confidentiality of information;
3 promote and support individual rights and choice within service delivery;
4 acknowledge individuals' personal beliefs and identity;
5 support individuals through effective communication.

These values are to be embedded in practice with the carer actively promoting them within her/his work. Looking at social divisions in relation to community care is a major theme of this book (see Chapters 2, 3 and 4) so the book will be particularly helpful in the areas of promoting anti-discriminatory or anti-oppressive practice and acknowledging individuals' personal beliefs and identity.

Another theme of the book (see especially Chapter 8) is user empowerment which will be helpful in relation to promoting and supporting individual rights and choice within service delivery.

Chapter 6 provides some information in relation to the core unit on the protection of individuals from abuse (unit Z1). Chapters 1 and 2 contain information which is relevant to the core unit and focuses on enabling clients to make use of available services and information (unit Y2).

The development of S/NVQs should ensure that users receive the same standards of care from all members of staff. Users should be able to expect a certain level of service from whoever is actually on duty.

GNVQs in Health and Social Care

1993 saw the introduction of a new award, GNVQs in 'Health and Social Care'. The material in this book will be helpful for Advanced Health and Social Care. This award contains eight mandatory units. The material in this book will be particularly useful for:

- Unit 1: Access, equal opportunities and client rights (see Chapters 2, 3, 4 and 8)
- Unit 6: Structure and practice in health and social care (see especially Chapters 1, 2 and 5)
- Unit 7: Care Plans (see especially Chapter 5).

The optional units vary between the Awarding Bodies but parts of this book will helpful in relation to:
- BTEC Optional Units 9, 12, 13 and 15

- City and Guilds Optional units 9, 10 and 16
- RSA Optional Units 12, 13, 14 and 15

Use of language

Workers in the National Health Service are generally used to describing the people they work with as 'patients'. Within Social Services Departments 'clients' has been most commonly used. Increasingly 'service user' has been used within both sectors and this phrase will be used in this book.

Policy variation

The material in this book has been written in relation to England. The policy context varies between England, Wales, Scotland and Northern Ireland. While much of the material is relevant to these contexts, some modification would be needed.

1

The background and legislation

Preview

This chapter covers:

○ what is meant by community care;
○ the mounting dissatisfaction with community care during the 1980s;
○ the key community care objectives within the National Health Service and Community Care Act 1990;
○ changes in the health service in the early 1990s;
○ an alternative vision of how services might be organized.

What do we mean by community care?

This chapter concentrates on the changes to community care brought about in the early 1990s. However community care has a longer history. There is no single definition of community care which causes some controversy. The definition in the 1989 White Paper, *Caring For People*, is as follows:

> Community care means providing the services and support which people who are affected by problems of ageing, mental illness, mental handicap or physical or sensory disability need to be able to live as independently as possible in their own homes, or in 'homely' settings in the community. The Government is firmly committed to a policy of community care which enables such people to achieve their full potential.

> (DoH, 1989b, p. 3)

This definition emphasizes certain groups of users that have been associated with community care in the past. These have sometimes been called 'priority groups'. While few would argue with the inclusion of the above groups, many would also wish to include people with drug or alcohol problems, people with HIV or AIDS, people who are terminally ill, women suffering from domestic violence, homeless people, and the needs of carers. Seen in this broader context, it is clear that community care covers a very wide area.

Another aspect of the debate about the definition of community care is discussion of which services are to be included. Community care draws on a range of services including domiciliary (home support services), day care, respite care (short-term breaks) and residential care. Should residential care be included in the spectrum of community care? While residential homes provide a permanent home for many people, they also increasingly provide emergency breaks or regular respite. In this way residential services are not simply alternatives to community care but can enable people to continue living in their own homes.

Language and community care

In discussing community care there are differing views on the use of appropriate language. In the quotation from the White Paper the term 'mental handicap' was used. Many people find this term unacceptable. Increasingly the terms 'learning difficulty' or 'learning disability' have been used. The important principle is to try to avoid language which offends people or gives people a negative label. This of course can change over time and it is important to be sensitive to these changes.

Why were changes needed to community care?

In the post-war period various governments made efforts to develop community care policies. These attempts were mainly directed towards moving people out of long-stay hospitals and into the community. There were also attempts to enable people to live in their own homes instead of having to be looked after in residential homes or hospitals. However the efforts were not pursued with great energy or determination and by the mid-1980s most commentators and politicians of all political parties agreed that community care was not being well-managed. Some of the key problems were:

- Health care and social care organizations were not working well together;
- Health care and social care authorities often had very different geographical boundaries;
- There were long-standing concerns about the effects of 'institutionalization' on people. This concern had arisen out of examples of bad practice, research studies and classic texts such as Goffman's *Asylums* (1968);
- Hospital closure programmes were not matched by the adequate building-up of community services to meet the needs of those discharged;
- The cost of people living in residential and nursing home care was rapidly expanding. This cost was often met entirely by the tax-payer;
- Nobody was required to do an assessment to check if someone really needed residential or nursing home care, with all the expense involved;
- Inadequate attention and support was given to carers who were usually close relatives and expected to care without any support from care professionals.

In 1985 the House of Commons' Social Services Committee produced a report, *Community Care With Special Reference to Adult Mentally Ill and Mentally Handicapped People*. This argued that the process of closing hospitals had run ahead of the development of satisfactory community care resources. The committee had heard a lot of anxieties and doubts about how community care was actually operating.

These anxieties about the operation of community care were reinforced in 1986 when an Audit Commission Report, *Making a Reality of Community Care*, was published. This report concentrated on provision for four 'priority groups'. These were (in the Report's language):

- elderly people;
- mentally ill people;
- mentally handicapped people;
- physically and sensorily handicapped people.

The Report powerfully outlined a whole range of problems associated with community care and concluded that:

> The one option that is not tenable is to do nothing about present financial, organizational and staffing arrangements . . . .. If this opportunity is not taken, a new pattern of care will emerge, based on private residential homes rather than a more flexible mix of services which includes residential care where appropriate. The result will be a continued waste of scarce resources and, worse still, care and support that is either lacking entirely, or inappropriate to the needs of some of the most disadvantaged members of society and the relatives who seek to care for them.
>
> (Audit Commission, 1986, p.4)

The Government responded to this report by asking Roy Griffiths to produce another report. Roy Griffiths had been involved in the retailing trade and had previously advised the government on health service reforms. This report, *Community Care: Agenda For Action*, better known as *The Griffiths Report*, was published in March, 1988. In it, Griffiths argued that a single organization should be in charge, or take the lead, in relation to community care. Griffiths' recommendation was that the organization best suited to this job was the local authority Social Services Department.

This message was initially not popular with a government which was anxious to reduce the power of local authorities. However in time it came to the same conclusion. As a result the White Paper, *Caring For People,* was published in November, 1989. This contained most of Griffiths' main recommendations.

Key objectives for community care

In the White Paper, *Caring For People*, the Government set out six key objectives:

- To provide services to enable people to live in their own homes wherever feasible and sensible;
- To ensure that service providers make practical support for carers a high priority;
- To provide proper assessment of needs and good care management (individual care plans);
- To promote the development of a flourishing independent sector alongside good quality public services;
- To make providers of services more accountable;
- To secure better value for money by introducing a new funding structure.

(DoH, 1989b, p. 5)

Four important community care publications

1 *Community Care With Special Reference To Adult Mentally Ill and Mentally Handicapped People*, House of Commons Social Services Committee, Second Report, 1985, HMSO.
2 *Making A Reality Of Community Care*, Audit Commission, 1986, HMSO.
3 *Community Care: Agenda For Action*, Roy Griffiths, 1988, HMSO.
4 *Caring For People*, Government White Paper, 1989, HMSO.

National Health Service and Community Care Act 1990

A few days after *Caring For People* appeared, the proposed legislation was published within the National Health Service and Community Care Bill. The National Health Service and Community Care Act (NHS&CC Act) successfully passed through Parliament in 1990. This Act laid down the way in which health care and community care are provided in the United Kingdom.

The main concern of this book is with the community care aspects of this Act. However the provision of health care and community care are closely intertwined, so it is important to cover both sets of changes. In this chapter most attention is given to the community care changes but some attention will also be given at the end to the health service changes.

The legislation itself

Part 111 of the 1990 Act (Sections 42–50) was concerned with community care and was entitled 'Community Care: England and Wales'. These few sections of the Act have provided the basis for community care provision. The key points are as follows:

- Sections 42–44 made changes to the National Assistance Act 1948 (S 26) and extended the powers of local authorities to make arrangements with private and voluntary homes for the care of those in need. Social Services Departments were to provide less themselves and to encourage and enable other organizations to make some of the provision. Changes were also made to the National Assistance Act 1948 (S 22) concerning charges for accommodation provided by local authorities.
- Section 46 placed a duty on local authorities to 'prepare and publish a plan for community care services in their area'. This plan was to be produced in consultation with District Health Authorities, Family Health Services Authorities and voluntary organizations.
- Section 47 placed a duty on local authorities to assess the care needs of those who may require community care services, involving other authorities/ services as appropriate. This duty was in addition to their existing duties under the Disabled Persons Act 1986.

- Section 48 stated that authorized officers may enter and inspect any premises in which community care services are, or are proposed to be, provided by a local authority or other bodies in arrangement with them.
- Section 49 allowed the transfer of NHS staff to local authority employment in connection with community care service arrangements.
- Section 50 empowered the Secretary of State to direct local authorities to establish complaints procedures, and to hold inquiries regarding social service provision for adults. This section also provided for the making of a specific grant to local authorities for the care of the mentally ill in the community.

It is worth emphasizing Section 47 which places a duty on local authorities to assess the care needs of those who may require community care services, involving other authorities/services as appropriate. When it talks about 'community care services' it is referring to those which local authorities can provide under the following Acts:

- **Part 111 of the National Assistance Act 1948**. This gave the local authority a duty to provide residential accommodation and welfare services for people aged eighteen or over who need it because of age, illness, disability or any other circumstances. It was also concerned with the provision of a wide range of welfare services for 'disabled' people.
- **Section 45 of the Health Services and Public Health Act 1968**. This required local authorities to make arrangements to promote the welfare of 'old people'.
- **Section 21 of and Schedule 8 to the National Health Service Act 1977**. This put a duty on local authorities to provide a home help service. It also gave powers to local authorities to provide other services such as day centres, meals, laundry services and social work support.
- **Section 117 of the Mental Health Act 1983**. This put a duty on the District Health Authority and the social services authorities to provide after-care services to people who have been detained in psychiatric hospital under Sections 3, 37, or 47 of the 1983 Act.

Key themes of the community care legislation

There were a number of themes embedded in the community care legislation. The following were especially important:

Assessment of need
Before important and expensive decisions are made about how and where someone should be cared for, a careful and thorough assessment of need should be carried out. This is covered by Section 47 of the Act and will be covered in Chapter 5.

Care management
A new system of organizing care was introduced to ensure that an effective provision of service is made for those in greatest need. This system is called 'care management' and will also be covered in Chapter 5.

Quality assurance

Under the legislation, Social Services Departments had to set up Inspection Units (Section 48) and complaints procedures (Section 50). These were attempts to try to ensure a better quality of service for users and will be discussed in Chapter 7.

Better planning and coordination

Services should be better planned and delivered with more coordination (Section 46).

Choice

More choice of services should be provided for the consumer or user. This theme is looked at in Chapter 8.

Mixed economy of care

Within this legislation is also embedded the belief that less social services provision should come from local authorities. Private companies or voluntary or charitable organizations should increase their provision. In this way a more competitive situation (or a 'market' situation) is created with alternative sources of provision being available.

Different sectors of care

The statutory sector
The statutory sector consists of those organizations that have been created by law. The NHS services and the local government services are sometimes referred to as the 'statutory sector'. They are mainly paid for by taxes.

The voluntary sector
The voluntary sector covers a very wide range of groups and provision. It includes charitable organizations and self-help organizations. Often, as well as providing services, these organizations lobby for change. Their funding can come from a range of sources which may include charitable giving.

The private sector
This is where commercial companies offer services on a fee-paying basis. For example, a major growth area of provision in the 1980s was private residential and private nursing home care.

The independent sector
This is a term sometimes used to include both the voluntary and private sectors.

Purchaser/provider

There is an idea that within the Social Services Departments there should be clearly separated functions between purchasing services and providing them. Through a process of contracting, departments may purchase services from a range of outside sources within the private and voluntary sector and sometimes from itself. This process is described in more detail in Chapter 7. Figure 1.1 illustrates the purchaser/provider split in the field of community care and shows how a market is created. The lead authority is the Social Services Department and part of that department will purchase services. The providers include:

- those parts of the Social Services Department that provide a service;
- services provided by agencies in the voluntary sector;
- services provided by the private sector.

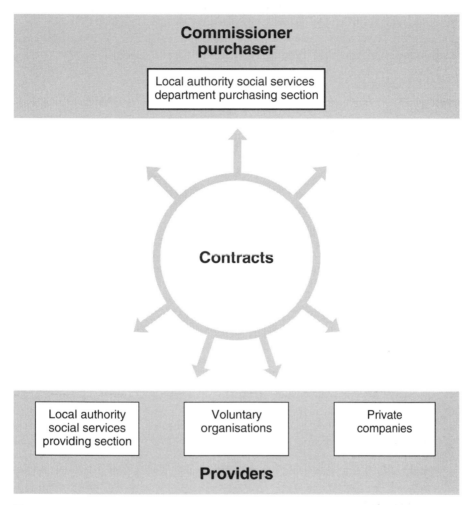

Figure 1.1: The way in which the purchaser/provider split affects the field of community care.

An initial critique

It is important to stress that the above changes have been controversial. Criticisms of the community care changes include:

- that the community care parts of the NHS&CC Act said nothing about the need for services to be sensitive to the needs of black people and people from ethnic minorities.

- that many disabled people have been disappointed that the changes do not enable them to be in charge of their own care by being paid money so that they can arrange it themselves.
- that services need coordination and that increasing competition between providers is not the best way to organize community care.
- that there is no advocacy system built into the legislation. Advocacy means enabling people to have their views heard and represented.

These issues and others will be returned to later in the book.

Stages of the implementation of community care changes

1991 — Two mechanisms for improving the quality of service were put in place. This involved the setting up of the inspection units and the complaints procedures.
1992 — Each local authority Social Services Department had to publish the first of its annual community care plans.
1993 — Social Services Departments took over lead responsibility in relation to community care. No-one could now enter a residential or nursing home at the taxpayer's expense without a full assessment. Social Services were given some additional funding for community care. They were also required to set up care management systems and separate purchaser/ provider functions.

The following fictional example will try to give a sense of what the changes implemented in April, 1993, have meant in practice.

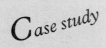

Mr Edwards lived with his wife for forty years in one house. His wife died in 1990. He has a daughter and family thirty miles away. The daughter visits about once a month or more often if there are any problems. Mr Edwards is less active than he used to be but he manages to shop for himself. He used to plays bowls at a local bowling club but stopped when he began to feel very short of breath. However he still goes to watch others and is well known at the club. He also calls into his local pub two or three times a week. He misses the company of his wife and feels quite depressed from time to time. He also gets rather anxious about paying his bills, but he is not in debt and manages on income support.

Mr Edwards has a bad fall. Nothing is broken but he is badly bruised and fairly immobile for 3–4 weeks. He moves in with his daughter but it would not be a satisfactory long-term arrangement as the house is too small to accommodate everyone satisfactorily. He becomes quite withdrawn and depressed.

In order to indicate how the legislative changes may affect what happens to Mr Edwards, a suggested outline is given of what happens to him before April, 1993, and then what happens to him after April, 1993.

Before April, 1993
The GP notes how depressed Mr Edwards is and suggests a private residential home he knows a few miles from where Mr Edwards lives. As Mr Edwards is on income support the fees for the home will automatically be paid by the Department of Social Security. The daughter likes this idea as she worries about

her father living alone. Also she is aware that he is very sorry for himself at present and she feels the company at the home may cheer him up. Mr Edwards is not very attracted to the idea but he does not want to be any trouble and agrees to a visit. He then agrees to go into the home. The Department of Social Security is notified. It will pay the fees for the residential home up to a maximum amount. The fees are £170 per week which are covered by the Department of Social Security (their maximum is £175) which also pays a personal allowance of £12.20 to Mr Edwards.

After April, 1993

The GP feels that a residential home would be good idea for Mr Edwards. However he knows he can only refer the situation to the local authority Social Services Department for an assessment. An assessment is coordinated by a care manager at the Social Services Department. She asks for and receives the views and opinions of Mr Edwards, the daughter, the GP, the district nursing service, the occupational therapist, and the home care organizer. It is decided by the care manager, on the basis of the information provided, that Mr Edwards does not require residential care. The care manager draws up a 'package of care' which involves some home care for a period and a weekly visit to a day centre. The home care is provided by the home care section of the Social Services Department and the day centre is run by a voluntary organization which has a contract with the local authority to provide a certain number of places. Mr Edwards makes some progress with his mobility and returns home. A home care worker attends three times a week, there is a weekly visit to a day centre and the daughter now visits twice a week. Mr Edwards makes a payment for the home care and the day care provision.

Comment on the changes

The following comments can be made about the situation after April 1993:

- There is a multi-disciplinary assessment by a care manager before any decision is made.
- The views of Mr Edwards are taken into account as part of this assessment.
- Mr Edwards is able to live at home with more support.
- The voluntary organization provides day care under a contract. This type of contractual arrangement has been an aspect of the changes.
- Mr Edwards makes a payment for the services – this type of charging for services has been encouraged by the changes and has created some controversy. Some say it is right that users should pay if they can afford it. Others argue that charging results in people who need services not receiving them. Some also put the view that welfare and health services should be free of charge on principle.
- The daughter gives more support. Some commentators have felt that the changes will put more pressure on this type of 'informal' and 'free' care which is often provided by women. This raises the question of whether community care changes are simply a way of the government saving money by expecting people in the community to do more caring.

Health Service changes

Most of the Sections of the National Health Service and Community Care Act 1990 were concerned with changes in the health service arising out of the White Paper, *Working For Patients* (DoH 1989a).

These were far-reaching changes which will be briefly summarized here.

The Health Service changes

1989 White Paper *Working For patients* (DOH, 1989a) published. This contains the proposals for change.
1990 NHS&CC Act, containing these changes, becomes law.
1991 (April) This is the date when the changes were implemented.

Figure 1.2 shows the structure of the NHS in England after April, 1991. Somewhat similar changes were introduced in Scotland, Northern Ireland and Wales.

The diagram shows the Secretary of State for Health at the top of the structure. The English Health Service is managed by the Department of Health Policy Board. Under this Board is the NHS Management Executive which was set up by the government to run the National Health Service.

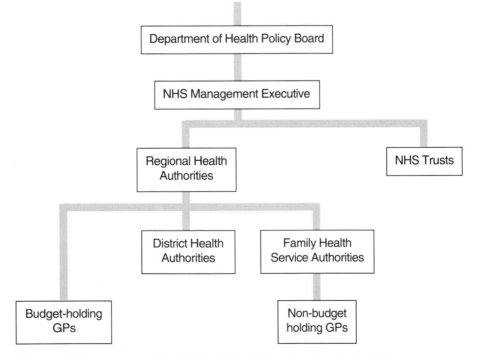

Figure 1.2: The structure of the National Health Service after April, 1991.

Under the NHS Management Executive are the NHS Trusts and Regional Health Authorities (RHAs). The 1990 Act led to the creation of self-governing NHS Trusts. These may be hospital trusts or community trusts (providing nursing and other health services within the community). Trusts employ their own staff, buy and sell their services and raise their own finance. Within a few years the great majority of NHS services had asked for and received trust status.

RHAs distribute funds to District Health Authorities (DHAs) and Family Health Service Authorities (FHSAs). They are the link between the National Health Service Management Executive and the more local DHAs and FHSAs. The main functions of RHAs are to determine how resources should be allocated, to monitor the efficiency of services and to mediate in any disputes.

The primary responsibility of DHAs is the health of local people. They manage any hospitals which have not become NHS trusts. They are required to assess health needs and decide how best they can be met. DHAs are given funds by RHAs to buy services on behalf of their residents. The amount of funding is determined by the size, age and relative health of that population. The DHA purchases care from providers which may include NHS Trusts, units directly managed by the DHA, or private or voluntary providers. Arrangements are made through contracts which set out the quantity, quality and cost of services to be provided throughout the year.

Family Health Service Authorities are responsible for primary health care services covering:

- general medical practitioners (GPs);
- practice nurses (nurses attached to and employed by GP practices);
- dentists;
- pharmacists;
- opticians.

The main function of FHSAs is to ensure that these groups do their work and are paid for it. FHSA services provide the main point of contact with the NHS for most people.

Under the NHS and Community Care Act 1990, GPs could become 'budget-holders' or 'fund-holders' and increasing numbers have been encouraged to take this step. GP budget-holders receive an annual budget directly from the RHA that enables them to buy certain hospital services and district nursing and health visiting services for their patients.

Central to the changes was the split between the purchasing and the providing of medical care. What was being created was an 'internal market' with some competition being generated within the structures of the old health service. There are similarities here with the community care changes and it was again a very radical break with the past. The idea was to try to make the NHS work more like private industry, where competition is supposed to keep prices low and quality high.

Figure 1.3 illustrates this split. It shows the proposed NHS structure for the mid and late 1990s (DOH, 1993d). The fourteen Regional Health Authorities are abolished, replaced by eight regional offices. DHAs and FHSAs will be encouraged to merge with the intention of creating stronger purchasers. These authorities and GP budget-holders can be seen as the purchasers buying from the providers. The providers are primarily the NHS trusts. The intention is that those on the purchasing side are in a position to drive bargains with the providers for better and more efficient services. Figure 1.3 also shows the GP non-budget-holders on the providing side. This is a decreasing number.

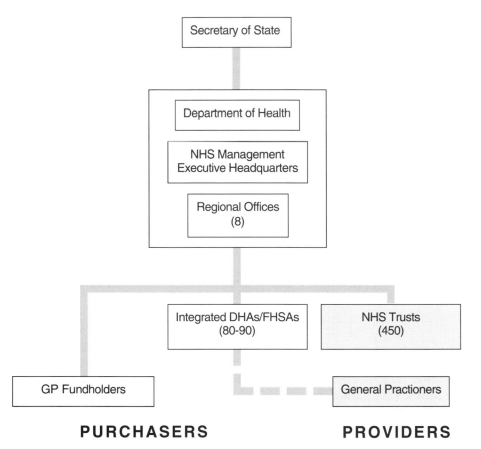

PURCHASERS   **PROVIDERS**

Figure 1.3: The new structure of the NHS (© CACI Limited, 1994. All Rights Reserved).

The Patient's Charter

The *Patient's Charter* was published in 1991 and was part of the Department of Health's contribution to the *Citizen's Charter* White Paper. The *Citizen's Charter* itself was an attempt by government to raise standards of service and to make the public services accountable to the users of those services.

The *Patient's Charter* set down patients' rights and a number of standards which are expected of health services. In 1993 this was extended to the FHSAs and GP services. At a local level it is likely that local charter standards have been set.

The health of the nation

A strategy for improving health was set out in the White Paper, *The Health of The Nation*, published in July 1992 (DoH, 1992a). This is concerned with the prevention of ill-health by health promotion and has a long-term aim of enabling people to live longer, healthier lives. There are targets for improvements in the following five areas:

- coronary heart disease and stroke;
- cancers;
- accidents;
- mental illness;
- HIV/AIDS and sexual health.

The strategy recognizes that there is a role for everyone in improving the health of the nation. This policy has obvious implications for community care. For example:

- If fewer people are disabled by strokes, heart disease or accidents there is less demand for community care resources.
- Community care resources for people with HIV/AIDS are under-developed. It is important both to provide community care for those with HIV/AIDS and also to develop preventative programmes and strategies.
- The human and social cost of mental distress is enormous. It is far better to work out strategies to reduce its occurrence rather than simply trying to deal with it once it has occurred. This is of course true of all five areas and the basic principle of the whole policy.
- Community care workers are in a good position to play an influential role in these preventive strategies.

An alternative perspective

It will be some time before it is possible to look back and assess the impact of the changes. Some have felt that patients of GPs who are not budget-holders have been receiving a poorer service. It is argued that the introduction of the market created a 'two-tier' system. This has happened because providers have responded more quickly to purchasers (budget-holding GPS) who might go elsewhere if they did not receive prompt attention. As a result the patients of GPs who are not budget-holders have received an inferior service.

The health and social care changes need to be seen as part of the wider agenda of government during the 1980s and early 1990s. The overall policy has been one of expanding the role of the market (those who support this policy are sometimes called the New Right). Nationalized industries have been privatized and market forces have been introduced into the services of the welfare state. This chapter has outlined how this process has been encouraged in the health and social services. In a critique of some of these developments Bob Holman writes:

> The New Right has been the dominant force in Britain during the last 15 years. In regard to social welfare, its policy-makers advocate curtailing the powers and costs of local authorities and shifting provision into the competitive market.
>
> (Holman, 1993, p. 94)

In *A New Deal For Social Welfare*, Holman is very critical of New Right values and policies. He argues for another set of values which he calls mutuality. Mutuality is:

*   the recognition of mutual obligation towards others;
*   the acceptance of common kinship;
*   expressed in joint action;
*   seeking a more equitable sharing of resources and responsibilities.

Taking mutuality as his foundation, Holman puts forward a vision in relation to the personal social services. Most of the ideas would be applicable to the broader range of services involved in community care. Holman argues that there should be properly-funded public services run by elected local authorities. The voluntary and private sector should supplement such services. Appropriate services should be promoted with the full involvement of people in the design. Further key points within Holman's vision are:

> *   Workers should try to equip families and individuals with the resources that enable them to cope with their own lives and prevent personal difficulties turning into bigger problems. The role of workers who are in direct contact with users should be that of identifying with them and speaking and acting on their behalf, in order to get the best services appropriate to their needs.
> *   Services should be available as facilities to neighbourhoods and not restricted to the few in greatest need. Community social work teams and family centres should be the main centres of social welfare activity.
> *   Agencies should develop strategies and staff skills to lessen the impact of poverty. There should be the acceptance of a responsibility to campaign against poverty. As part of this strategy, some priority should be given to strengthening and extending local community groups.
>
> (Holman, 1993, p. 94)

*A*ctivity

Under the NHS&CC Act 1990, each local authority had to produce a community care plan in close consultation and cooperation with DHAs and FHSAs. It also had to involve consultation with user groups. Obtain a copy of the latest community care plan in your area. The central office of your local authority Social Services Department should be able to let you have a copy. Many local libraries will also have copies for reference. As you read it consider the following questions:

- What is said about the relationships between local authorities, DHAs and FHSAs and their contribution to community care?
- What is said about consultation with users, carers and private and voluntary sector providers in the preparation of the report?
- What is said about care management?
- What impressed you about the report?
- Was there anything that you felt was missing from the report?

*A*ctivity

Contact your local FHSA, DHA, or Community Health Council and ask what they can provide you with in relation to the Patient's Charter. They should be able to let you have a copy of the summary of the national Patient's Charter and details of any local charter of agreed standards.

Key questions

1 What do we mean by community care?
2 Why were changes needed to community care?
3 What were the key changes brought about to community care by the NHS&CC Act 1990?
4 What were the main changes brought about to health services by the NHS&CC Act 1990?
5 What criticisms can you begin to identify in relation to these changes?

Further reading

Audit Commission, *Making A Reality Of Community Care*, HMSO, London, 1986. This covers what was wrong with community care and why something needed to be done. Appendix A of the report gives a brief summary of community care in the post-war period.

Department of Health, *Caring For People* (DoH 1989b), HMSO, London, 1986. This White Paper has been the basis of the changes which have taken place during the 1990s. Both this document and the Audit Commission Report can be criticized for their lack of coverage of race issues.

Meredith, B. *The Community Care Handbook*, Age Concern, London, 1993. There are a number of guides to the White Paper, the legislation and the changes. This one is clear and comprehensive.

Holman, B. *A New Deal For Social Welfare*, Lion Publishing, Oxford, 1993. This was referred to in this chapter and contains a powerful critique of New Right ideas applied to social welfare. It attacks the idea of the contract culture and the market philosophy and proposes alternatives based on values of mutuality.

2
Who does the caring?

Preview

This chapter explores who is involved in community care. It considers:

○ the distinction between informal and formal care;
○ who the informal carers are;
○ the ways in which social divisions affect caring;
○ the contribution of the formal sector to caring as regards the contribution of the statutory, voluntary and private sectors to caring;
○ the need for good communication and cooperation between all the elements of the formal sector;
○ the need for effective and sensitive work with carers from the informal sector.

Who is doing the caring?

Formal care is care provided on an organized and paid basis through health and welfare agencies. **Informal care** is provided on an unpaid basis usually from feelings of love, obligation and duty. The majority of informal care is provided within the context of family and marital relationships.

There are important questions about the balance of formal and informal care and the relationship between them. How far do family members have a duty to care for the older or more disabled members of their family and how far should the state and government help? Who should be responsible for the costs and who should make the decisions when there are deep conflicts of interest?

The care provided within any society will vary according to the nature and history of that society. There are no absolute answers and the solutions that each society devises will change over time. It is also the case that different communities within any one society provide different levels of informal care.

In the early 1980s Government publications moved from talking about care 'in' the community to care 'by' the community. This was a shift of emphasis and one way you can see the change is by looking carefully at the quotation below, taken from the 1981 White Paper, *Growing Older*:

> Whatever level of public expenditure proves practicable and however it is distributed, the primary sources of support and care for elderly people are informal and voluntary. These spring from personal ties of kinship, friendship and neighbourhood. They are

irreplaceable. It is the role of public authorities to sustain and where necessary develop
– but never to displace – such support and care. Care in the community must increasingly mean care by the community.

(DHSS, 1981)

The above quotation (with the stress on *by* the community) is often given in
discussions of community care because it points to the key issue of *who* is doing
the caring. Social scientists have always emphasized how much care has been
done by the community. The above statement from government in 1981 recognized the central role of unpaid carers and marked a shift in emphasis of policy.

Who are the unpaid carers?

Much of the research that has been done on carers has been small-scale, and
generalizations have been made from these small-scale studies. The 1985
General Household Survey was the first large-scale study to include detailed
information on Britain's carers. The study showed that:

- there are six million carers in the United Kingdom;
- one adult in seven is a carer;
- 15% of all adult women are carers;
- 12% of all adult men are carers;
- 3% of adults in the UK (about 1.4 million people) devote at least 20 hours
  per week to caring.

Differing perceptions of community care

Not surprisingly, different members of the community care network may have
a different understanding of community care. For example:

- Unpaid carers may view community care as being what they do.
- People employed by Social Services Departments may think community
  care means the provision of residential care, day-care, domiciliary care, or
  respite care.
- People within the health sector may associate community care with district
  nursing, health visiting, the provision of chiropody, GP and other services.

The need for partnership

The list below shows some of the people who might assist a frail, elderly person
to continue living in the community. The list shows that most frail older people
in the community are supported by a mixture of formal services and informal
carers including:

- doctor;
- partner/relatives;
- neighbours/friends;

- district nurse;
- home care worker.

The paid carers in this short list (and it could be much longer) are:

- the home care worker from local authority social services;
- the district nurse (probably from the community trust);
- the GP (probably a budget-holder).

You can begin to see the range of formal agencies involved. These are not just individual people but professionals belonging to organizations with their own rules and regulations. One of the key questions in relation to community care is how well do workers from these different organizations work together in providing an effective service for older people? The two boxes below outline two situations: one where there are poor relationships and one where relationships are good.

Possibility 1 (Characteristics of poor relationships)
These could be:

- lack of awareness by the paid workers of the strains and pressures on the unpaid relative carers;
- poor relations between the professional workers;
- strain between the GP and the Social Services office;
- lack of clarity over 'who does what' between the nurse and the home care worker;
- insensitivity of the home care worker to the particular needs of the elderly person;
- relatives being unsympathetic to the pressures on the home help.

Possibility 2 (Characteristics of good relationships)
These could be:

- sensitivity by all the paid workers to the pressures on the unpaid relatives;
- good relations between all the paid workers achieved by hard work at a local level over a number of years;
- good links and understanding between those who provide the different sorts of paid care at the local level;
- efforts made by all the paid workers to consider the particular and individual needs of the person;
- everyone's awareness of the strengths and limitations of the contributions made by others through good communication.

What is clear is that different carers (paid and unpaid) are making different contributions. Community care works well where there is an effective partnership between the informal and formal sectors and where the needs of the user are central. Two of the key concepts used to describe this are 'involvement' and 'partnership'.

A central intention of the changes in community care in the early 1990s was that the structures should develop in a way that enables service-users and their close relatives to express their wishes and needs. Their views and aspirations should receive greater consideration in the planning of services that are provided. They should be **involved**. A three-way **partnership** should therefore develop between the service-user, the carer and the services which are to be provided by the formal sector.

The role of unpaid carers in providing community care

One of the key objectives of the community care changes was to ensure that carers were offered both practical and emotional support by service providers. The White Paper, *Caring For People*, pointed out that:

- most care is provided by family, friends and neighbours;
- many carers need help to be able to manage what can be a heavy burden;
- carers' lives can be made much easier if the right support is there at the right time;
- a key responsibility of providers of statutory services should be to do all they can to assist and support carers;
- helping carers to maintain their valuable contribution to the spectrum of care is both right and a sound investment;
- help may take the form of providing advice and support as well as practical services such as day, domiciliary and respite care.

(DoH, 1989b, p. 9)

The Government recognized that its policy of care in the community could only work if carers were regarded not as an extra resource, but as a central part of the mainstream health and community care arrangements. This means that carers themselves require resources in order to function effectively.

Volunteers and informal care

'Volunteers' are a part of the informal sector who in some situations can provide invaluable support. For example the Buddy Service is based on volunteers. This service was developed by The Terence Higgins Trust in Greater London to provide people with AIDS with someone who could give reliable friendship and support when needed. A Buddy is a volunteer who makes a commitment to become a friend to someone with AIDS and to see them perhaps two or three times a week. They are trained by the Trust to listen, talk and probably help with some practical tasks.

Responding to the needs of carers was therefore recognized as central to an effective community care strategy. If community care was to work, the needs of carers would have to be addressed more systematically and with far greater commitment.

The House of Commons Social Services Committee stressed the importance of carers in its 1990 Community Care report:

For too long carers have been the unrecognized partners in our welfare system. Their services have been taken for granted. They have been regarded as a resource, but not as people with their own needs.

(House of Commons, 1990, p. xx)

Informal carers and the law

You may have expected that, after this type of discussion and these public statements, the provision and support given to carers would form an important part of the NHS&CC Act 1990. However, despite this official recognition of the difficult job undertaken by carers they are given scant attention in the Act itself.

As the NHS&CC Act was progressing through Parliament, Government minister, Virginia Bottomley, acknowledged this herself when she told the Social Services Select Committee:

Although not enshrined in legislation, the role of the carer most clearly will be given the priority that they deserve in all our guidance about assessment, about community care plans and about all the other aspects of these proposals.

(House of Commons, 1990, p. v)

Other people and groups felt that these official statements were not enough and campaigned vigorously for the position of carers to be protected in the legislation itself. For example, the Association of County Councils pointed out the need for properly prepared and costed proposals. They argued strongly that this was 'a serious omission' from the White Paper. They felt that well-meaning statements about doing all possible to assist carers needed to be more strongly built into the legislation. Otherwise they would contribute to raising expectations which could not be met.

Section 8 of the 1986 *Disabled Persons Act* requires Social Services Departments 'to have regard to' the abilities of a carer to continue to provide care for a disabled person undergoing an assessment from the local authority. A report on the Act was published in 1990 by the Social Services Inspectorate which showed that only one-fifth of Social Services Departments had an agreed policy on the operation of Section 8 (DoH, 1990c).

This is an important piece of legislation to see properly implemented because there is no other in this area. One commentator wrote:

This is the first piece of legislation in history that explicitly recognises that carers have needs, and as such it is important that its full potential is realised by all those wishing to see an improvement in service provision for carers. We believe it can be used to help tilt the balance between rhetoric and reality firmly towards the latter.

(Simpson, 1991, p. 20)

Changes in patterns of living

People sometimes comment that in our society there is less caring than there used to be and that younger people no longer want to care for older or disabled people in the community. The point has already been made about different societies coping with the needs of frail and vulnerable people in different ways. Changes in caring patterns also vary over time. It may not be that people are less caring but rather that society is changing and this has implications for who is available to care. As society changes, the level of informal care available also changes.

The following changes in the patterns of living are likely to have a considerable impact on how much informal care is available:

- Divorce rates doubled during the 1970s. During the 1980s around 150 thousand married couples a year experienced a divorce.
- The proportion of children born outside marriage has risen dramatically in recent years. Between 1964 and 1990, the number of births outside marriage increased from 63 thousand to 200 thousand.
- One in four children today will experience a parental divorce before their sixteenth birthday.
- Almost one in five families with dependent children are lone parent families.

(FPSC, 1991)

Who will care in the future?

We do not know the extent to which these changes in living patterns will have an impact on community care. Some impact seems likely but at present we can only guess at the answers to questions such as:

- Will the increase in divorce mean that less informal care is given by the marriage partner than in the past?
- Will children feel the same duty and obligation to care for their parents in a situation where the marriage broke up?
- Will step-children feel the same obligation to care for step-parents?

Social divisions and informal care

Many users and carers suffer from and have suffered from discrimination and oppression. This is not simply individuals suffering for a particular reason. It is rather that certain groups in society suffer from poor treatment and discrimination. Divisions are created because some groups have power while others do not.

Social divisions

A useful and common categorization of social divisions is based on gender, class, sexual orientation, disability, age and race. Groups within these categories are in some ways 'oppressed' by society as a whole and by structures which do not treat them equally and fairly.

Of the various social divisions it is gender which has dominated much of the debate about informal care. Some writers from a feminist perspective have seen informal care as necessarily oppressive to women. Informal caring is seen as unpaid labour within the family, often provided by the female spouse or daughter.

There has been a strong debate about the gender aspects of community care. Questions have been posed such as:

- Do community care policies inevitably mean more pressure and exploitation of women?
- Is it possible for there to be a non-sexist approach to community care?

More recently it has been argued that the debate is more complicated and that research on caring has not looked at the variety of situations among women carers.

Social class and the experience of caring

The limitations of assuming that all women carers share a similar experience are made obvious in the way in which social class influences the experience of being a carer. Middle-class carers usually have access to more and better resources than working-class carers. They are probably in a better position to buy in services, have a greater knowledge of what is available and skills to ensure that they receive what they are entitled to. They may be able to present their situation in the best way to ensure that their problem receives proper consideration. They are more likely to have jobs in which the working hours can be adjusted so that they are more compatible with managing to care in a family (Atkin, 1992, p. 57).

It is rather surprising that class has figured very prominently in debates about inequalities in health over the past twenty years but has played a much smaller role in the discussion and analysis of informal caring.

Age and the experience of caring

The impact of social class on the experience of caring is magnified by the way in which social class and age intertwine to disadvantage older people. The patterns of disadvantage which older people face are well-documented. These include bad housing, poverty and low income, social isolation, low social status and relative lack of power. What is probably less well known is that many carers are themselves of retirement age, and are becoming carers at a time when they might have expected life to become easier. Many people in their 50s, 60s and

70s find themselves caring for parents or partners. The fact that the carers themselves are old has considerable implications for the experience of caring. This is particularly the case in relation to the impact of poorer health on the carer. Atkin writes,

> Older carers are more likely to be in poor health than younger carers and therefore experience greater difficulty with physical care tasks.
>
> (Atkin, 1992, p. 53)

Atkin also points out that as well as health worries, older carers are more likely to have concerns about what will happen to the person they are responsible for when they die or are unable to cope any longer.

The patterns of disadvantage and health problems experienced by many older carers may be made worse by the response of the service providers themselves to older carers. They may for instance feel that the carer is too old to care, or be more inclined to suggest residential care as a solution. Workers involved with older carers need to assess each situation in its own right and avoid making assumptions based simply on the age of the carer (Atkin, 1992, p. 53).

In considering the issue of age and caring it should also be noted that some young children take on a considerable caring role.

Gender: difference and division

Graham has argued that research on caring has missed out on some of the wider feminist debates of the 1980s on differences and divisions among women. Those debates have looked at the way in which analyses in the past have under-emphasized divisions of race and class, sexuality and disability among women (Graham, 1993).

There are some areas of caring that we know little about. Studies have mainly been of white, heterosexual women in family networks. We know little, for example, about caring in lesbian relationships. Graham notes,

> While feminist studies of caring have explored the consequences of having family ties, they have paid less attention to the experiences of lesbians seeking and providing care for women outside the nuclear family.
>
> (Graham, 1993, p. 128)

Gender, disability and caring

In relation to gender and disability there is a potential conflict of interests between women confined to the home as carers and disabled people (also often women) trying to achieve a greater degree of independent living. If community care only results in greater exploitation of women carers then some writers have suggested that perhaps residential care should be the solution (Dalley, 1988).

However for many disabled people this is an outrageous suggestion and their key demand is the 'right' to live in the community rather than in residential care. The issue here is whether exercising that 'right' to live in the community necessarily puts stress and pressure on family carers. Thus a further key demand for disabled people is for the right to the kind of 'personal assistance' which they can choose (Morris, 1991, p. 168).

There is a tension here which is often at the heart of community care. For health and social care workers it can throw up the issue of whether they become part of the pressure on family carers to do more or become part of the pressure to provide more resources to enable people to live as independently as they wish.

Disability and carers

Well-designed toilets and bathrooms may reduce the need for informal carers to be helping with aspects of personal care. Accessible transport systems may mean that disabled people can travel independently. Any interventions which serve to reduce disability and 'dependence' also serve to reduce the numbers of informal carers.

(Parker, 1992, p. 16)

Caring and gender

It is often assumed that almost all carers are women and that the issue hardly ever affects men. Although it is undoubtedly true that the majority of carers are women, one of the surprising results of the General Household Survey data was the extent to which men were involved in caring. Twelve per cent of adult men identified themselves as carers in contrast with fifteen per cent of adult women. Detailed analysis of the data however, showed that most of these male carers were spouses and/or that they were involved in the lighter aspects of caring. Care between the generations involving long hours and close personal care was still shown to be carried out largely by women.

Although there are undoubtedly many male carers, this does not however mean that the position of carers is not a gender issue. The response of services, the need for support, the attitudes of neighbours, relatives and the carers themselves may well be different depending on whether or not a man or woman is the primary carer. Two key points for health and social care workers are:

- The need to be careful not to disadvantage female carers by automatically giving more support to male carers (Atkin, 1992, p. 52).
- The need to be conscious that often these attitudes also affect the carers themselves. Female carers may feel that they cannot ask for services they really need or are entitled to. Male carers may feel more strongly that it is their right to have help.

Race and caring

One of the main reasons why carers have been a low priority is because the caring takes place in private and is therefore invisible as a political issue. This problem of invisibility is made worse for black people because they often face the additional problems of inappropriate and insensitive services (see Chapter 4).

In the older white population, women heavily outnumber men. Among some black communities, however, older men outnumber and will continue to outnumber older women because of the differences of migration patterns in the 1950s and 1960s when more male migrants came into the United Kingdom (Atkin and Rollings, 1993, p. 8).

A key factor influencing the pattern and experiences of caring is the structure, size and location of existing family networks. For some women, caring can be a negative and oppressive experience. Graham points out that the experience of black women may be different. She suggests that their own experiences are often influenced by the absence of a family network, perhaps because of migration factors. Much of their struggle, in these cirmumstances, may be to create a family network rather than finding the demands of such a structure oppressive (Graham, 1993, p. 128).

Checklist for health and social care workers

In their relationships with carers, health and social care workers need to ask themselves whether they are responding in a way that is based only on their own values and attitudes or responding to the needs of the carers. The kind of questions they should ask themselves are:

- Am I reinforcing the view that women are natural carers?
- Am I giving more help and attention to a carer because the carer is a man?
- Am I considering the possibility that the caring relationship may be gay or lesbian?
- Is my view of the abilities of older people realistic and sensitive to each situation?
- Am I being sensitive to the particular needs of black carers?

The formal sector and community care

It was noted at the beginning of the chapter that most community care is provided by carers in the informal sector. However a significant contribution is also made by the formal sector. The formal sector is made up of the following parts or sectors which were introduced in Chapter 1:

- the statutory sector;
  1 the National Health Service;
  2 local authority services, especially those services provided by Social Services Departments;
- the voluntary sector;
- the private sector.

The statutory sector

The National Health Service
Chapter 1 mentioned the three kinds of health authority and the various health services provided by them:

- Regional Health Authority;
- District Health Authority;
- Family Health Services Authority.

There are many people from the health services concerned with community care but the key personnel are:

- **General Practitioner (GP):** the family doctor who can put patients in touch with a range of health services.
- **Community or District Nurse:** helps with practical nursing in the community. This would include, for example, toileting, giving injections, changing dressings, turning and lifting.
- **Community Psychiatric Nurse:** visits and advises people with mental health problems and their carers. Will give any necessary medication.

Local authority services

Within local authority Social Services offices key personnel involved with delivering community care are:

Home care workers (sometimes called home helps or domiciliary care workers)
Home care workers help with housework, preparing meals, shopping and increasingly personal care such as help with dressing and washing. As home care workers have undertaken more personal care, the boundaries between home care and nursing have become blurred.

Occupational therapists
Occupational therapists are there to assist disabled people to live in the community. They will assess people for various aids and adaptations such as raised toilet seats, bath rails, ramps and lifts.

Social workers
The role of social workers has been changing over recent years. They have often played a role in enabling people to gain access to some of the services listed below. With the community care changes some of them have taken on the role of care managers whose job it is to arrange and coordinate packages of care.

Social Services Departments also provide a range of other services which are important for community care. These include:

- day centres;
- mobile meals;
- residential homes which can provide long-term care and short-term 'respite' care;
- luncheon clubs.

Voluntary sector

The voluntary sector covers an extraordinary range of groups and provision. It includes charitable organizations and self-help organizations. As well as providing services, they often lobby for change at the same time. Their funding can come from a range of sources which may include charitable giving. Where services are provided, this is increasingly done through 'contracts' with the statutory sector. This is covered in more detail in Chapter 7.

Voluntary sector example – Crossroads

The first Crossroads Care Attendant Scheme was established in Rugby in 1974. 'Crossroads Care Attendant Schemes' have grown rapidly, and by 1994 there were over 200 schemes providing over two million care hours in a year to over 22,000 families regularly. The schemes provide a service which is aimed at relieving the strain on carers of disabled people of any age by providing them with practical help in their own home. Pat Osborne who was the director until 1988 has said that what Crossroads did 'was to create a new worker within the community who was a hybrid between a nursing auxiliary and a home help'. Key elements of the scheme are that the times are requested by the carer and that support is ongoing, reliable and flexible.

These organizations often rely on a good deal of work put in by people who are not paid. However most of them employ people and can be quite large organizations. Examples of such organizations are Mind, Age Concern and Mencap. Small self-help projects may or may not have the finance to employ anyone but count as part of the voluntary sector.

Carers also have voluntary organizations that represent their interests. One such organization is the Carers National Association which has a national office and many local branches. The same is true of the Alzheimer's Disease Society which is an organization for and of carers of people who suffer from the disease.

The private sector

Individuals and companies in the private sector offer a wide range of services on a fee-paying basis. Private residential and private nursing home care was a major growth area of provision during the 1980s. A lot of this was financed by the special rates of income support for people entering these forms of care who had limited means. With the changes brought in by the 1990 NHS&CC Act a number of these organizations closed down. Some successfully diversified into private home care work (domiciliary care) and other areas.

The need for coordination within the formal sector

One of the problems with community care in the past has been that so many varied services have been provided by a range of organizations. Sometimes these organizations have different geographical boundaries and often they are staffed by professionals with a somewhat different professional outlook. As a way of illustrating this, study the list of possible services for a frail, elderly person in Figure 2.1 on the next page.

This is a long (and not necessarily comprehensive) list with various providers. It illustrates the potential difficulty for the user in obtaining an appropriate range of services in a coordinated manner. One of the intentions of care management is to improve this coordination. A few points in relation to the list are:

- The situation does keep changing and it varies according to different areas.
- In terms of providers, there is an increasing development of 'private' agencies. There are, for example, an increasing number of private home care schemes.

Service	Possible Provider
Home help or home care	Social Services, private
Aids and adaptations	Social Services – occupational therapy service
Meals Service	Social Services or Voluntary (e.g. Women's Royal Voluntary Society, local service for Muslim elders) or private
Counselling/social work	Social Services – social worker, voluntary
Nursing	District Nursing Service under District Health Authority, NHS community trust
General Practitioner	Family Health Service Authority or as a GP budget-holder
Health Screening	G.P. Practice Nurse, Family Health Service Authority
Health Visitor	District Health Authority, NHS community trust
Putting-to-bed Service	District Health Authority, NHS community trust, Social Services, voluntary or private
Night-sitting service	District Health Authority, NHS community trust, voluntary or private
Day care	Social Services, District Health Authority, NHS community trust, voluntary or private
Respite care	Social Services, District Health Authority, NHS community trust, voluntary, private
Chiropody	District Health Authority, NHS community trust
Sheltered housing	Housing Authority, Housing Association, voluntary, private
Bath service	District Health Authority, NHS community trust, private
Incontinence laundry	Health Authority, Social Services
Physiotherapy	District Health Authority, NHS community trust
Domiciliary dentistry	Family Health Service Authority
Community psychiatric nursing	District Health Authority, NHS community trust
Optician	District Health Authority, NHS community trust, Family Health Service Authority
Community alarm service	Housing authority
Continence adviser	District Health Authority, NHS community trust

Figure 2.1: List of possible services for frail, elderly people.

• As will be evident from the above list, it will now sometimes be DHAs and sometimes NHS community trusts that will make provision.
• Not included here are residential homes, nursing homes, hospital care and, of course, the contribution of the informal sector.

Services for mentally distressed people

There are different formal providers (statutory, voluntary and private) and different places in which the care is provided (service settings). For each user-group the types of service settings will vary somewhat. For example, Figure 2.2 shows the service settings for adults who have or are suffering problems of mental health or mental distress. In this chart the three broad service settings identified are:

• those which provide care at home;
• those which provide care in a day-care setting;
• those which provide care in a residential setting.

	Acute/emergency care	Rehabilitation/continuing care
Home-based	Intensive home support Emergency duty teams Sector teams	Domiciliary services Key workers Care management
Day care	Day hospitals	Drop-in centres Support groups Employment schemes Day care
Residential support	Crisis accommodation Acute units Local secure units	Ordinary housing Unstaffed group homes Adult placement schemes Residential care homes Mental nursing homes 24 hour NHS accommodation Medium secure units High security units

Figure 2.2: Services for mentally distressed people (DoH, 1993a, p. 71).

Most of the services in Figure 2.2 are provided by the statutory sector. However some (for example, domiciliary services, drop-in centres, support groups, employment schemes and day care) may be provided by the voluntary sector. Some (for example, residential care homes and mental nursing homes) may be provided by the private sector. Part of the intention of the early 1990s reforms was to see more services contracted out to the voluntary and private sector.

Services for people with HIV/AIDS

There is a range of formal services for mentally distressed people although they are usually stretched and in short supply. For people with HIV infection on the other hand this is often not the case. Figure 2.3 gives an overview of some of the services that may be required for adults with HIV infection. In the left column are services for those who are HIV positive but have not developed symptoms of HIV related disease. Listed in the other three columns are services that may be required for people with symptomatic HIV disease or AIDS.

The diagram is shown as an example of the range of services that may be required by one group of service-users. Again some may be provided by the statutory services but some will be provided by the voluntary and private sectors. Equally important are the values and attitudes of workers in these settings. People with HIV/AIDS suffer from considerable discrimination and

Asymptomatic	*Acutely ill*	*Chronically ill*	*Terminally ill*
Counselling and medical evaluation	Psychosocial and ongoing medical care	Psychosocial and ongoing medical care	Psychosocial ongoing medical care
Testing facilities partner notification	In-patient services	Day care Out-patients	Intensive home nursing
Education	Out-patient services	Transportation	In-patient or hospice services
Out-patient follow-up and treatment including prophylaxis	Rehabilitation services	Emergency telephone assistance	Bereavement services to family, friends
Psychological and other support services	Home care services	Home delivered meals	Care services for children whose parents are terminally ill
	Childcare support as necessary	Other practical support in the home	
		some home nursing	
		sheltered housing	
		residential or respite care	
		childcare support as necessary	

Figure 2.3: Overview of some of the services for adults with HIV (DoH, 1993b, p. 59).

prejudice, often based on fear and lack of knowledge. Workers need to be knowledgeable about the disease and work to counter prejudice and discrimination.

Bringing it together

This chapter has looked at the contribution to community care by unpaid carers and by paid carers. One of the great challenges of community care is trying to achieve a situation where the appropriate services go to the service-user in an efficient and cost-effective way. These formal services need to link in sensitively and supportively to the contributions being made by unpaid carers. There are three main options for achieving this:

- Try to obtain better coordination by structural reorganization. For example, the NHS and the local authority provision for community care could be brought together within one integrated unit.
- Creating multi-disciplinary teams at the local level. Workers at the local level come together in teams in order to share their expertise and increase understanding of each others' contribution.
- A Social Services Department having a lead role in coordinating arrangements and somebody taking the key role in ensuring a good assessment takes place followed by setting up a coordinated 'package of care' for the user.

The changes of the early 1990s did not involve the first option of structural reorganization. In relation to the second option there have been experiments and initiatives with multi-disciplinary teams which go back to the 1970s. These teams are continuing and the early 1990 changes have neither encouraged nor discouraged this option for improved coordination. It is however the third option which was the cornerstone of the changes of the early 1990s. Social Services departments were given the 'lead' role in coordinating arrangements and care managers were to have the central role in ensuring that appropriate packages of care were brought together. Chapter 5 will look into this in more detail.

*A*ctivity

You probably know an unpaid carer. If it can be done sensitively and inoffensively, talk to them about:

- why they care;
- the costs of caring — both financial and personal;
- how they feel they have been treated by any paid worker they have been involved with.

You probably also know someone who works in one of the paid services concerned with community care described in this chapter. Make a point of asking them about:

- the work they do;
- their relationships with other paid workers;
- their relationships with unpaid carers;
- their views on what works well in relation to community care and their views on what the problems are.

Key questions

1   What is the difference between formal and informal care?
2   In what way do issues relating to social division affect informal carers?
3   What are the different parts of the formal sector?
4   What services might be available within the formal sector for a frail older person?
5   What service settings are there for people suffering problems of mental distress?
6   What service settings are there for people suffering from HIV/AIDS?

Further reading

Wilson, J. *Caring Together*, King's Fund, London, 1988. This is a useful publication giving guidelines for carers' self-help and support groups. It is full of ideas on setting up a carers' self-help group.

Gunaratnam, Y. *Call To Care*, King's Fund, London, 1991. This has been produced in consultation with Asian carers of elderly people. It provides information and advice on services and welfare benefits, on dealing with discrimination and racial harassment, and how to get help when carers cannot speak English. It is available in English, Bengali, Gujarati, Punjabi, and Urdu from the Health Education Authority.

Twigg, J. *Carers: Research And Practice*, HMSO, London, 1992. This is a useful summary of research studies and literature on carers. It is especially valuable if you wish to look into the subject of carers in more depth.

HMSO, *Social Welfare*, HMSO, London, 1993. Many social policy books will give additional information on the health service, personal social services, the voluntary and private sectors. This HMSO publication describes in straightforward terms the organization and function of the National Health Service, the personal social services and the social security system.

3

Normalization, disability and community care

Preview

This chapter covers:

○ the idea of normalization;
○ self-advocacy and citizen advocacy;
○ disability and social oppression;
○ self-organization by disabled people;
○ independent living and disabled people.

Normalization

In the past, people with learning difficulties have often been shut away in large hospitals. The idea of 'normalization' grew as an attempt to react against this policy and integrate these people back into society.

The concept of normalization had its origins in Denmark in the late 1950s. The ideas influenced the provision of services in Denmark and Sweden in the 1960s. In the 1970s and 1980s, in the United States, Wolf Wolfensberger proposed and then developed more elaborate ideas on normalization which he later referred to as 'social role valorization'. This is now his preferred description but many people still use the term 'normalization'.

The aim of normalization is simply to treat all people as equal citizens, with equal rights and equal access to valued social roles. Normalization attempts to change the fact that some groups of people have often been regarded as of lesser value in society. Members of such groups are likely to be treated unfairly and unjustly. Thus discrimination is one consequence of being devalued. A devalued group is sometimes described as an 'oppressed group'.

A vicious circle can be set up in which a member of an oppressed group is exposed to widely-held stereotypes about that group and comes to believe that the stereotypes are true.

Stereotyping

Stereotyping means placing people together and regarding them and treating them as if they were all the same. Usually stereotyping operates in a negative way and gives an unfavourable view of a group of people.

When people hear negative views about themselves and receive negative behaviour, they can over time come to accept that view of themselves. Another word for this is 'internalization'. Normalization is one tool for identifying, analysing and reversing this vicious circle which may trap people who are elderly, people who have a physical, sensory or learning disability or people who are mentally ill.

Examples of internalization

- Older people believing that they have no useful role to play;
- Unemployed people believing that it is their fault that they are unemployed;
- Black people believing that they are inferior to white people;
- Disabled people feeling second-class compared to able-bodied people.

The ideas of normalization are relevant to all adult groups in the field of community care. However the origins of normalization were in the area of working with people with learning difficulty and much of the following discussion will focus on this area of work.

An ordinary life

The principle of normalization has been a force for change in the United Kingdom, especially for people with learning difficulties. It has also contributed to the 'ordinary life' movement in the United Kingdom. This movement had its origins in the principle that people with severe learning difficulties should live ordinary lives. John O'Brien has described the implications of normalization in relation to what services should try to achieve or accomplish for users. He has identified five major service accomplishments which are a practical application of the 'ordinary life' values for people with learning difficulties. These are:

Community presence
The right to live and spend time in the community rather than in residential, day or leisure facilities which segregate them from other members of society.

Competence
In order for a full and rewarding life to be lived in the local community, many will require help to learn more skills and have access to a wider range of activities.

Choice
A high-quality service will give priority to enhancing the choices available to people and generally protecting their human rights.

Respect
Services can have an important role in helping people enjoy the same status as other valued members of society.

Relationships
Help and encouragement is needed to mix with other non-disabled people in their daily lives.

(King's Fund Centre, 1991, p. 45)

These are powerful and radical principles when they are applied to much of the provision which has been available for people with learning disabilities. Since the 1970s people with learning difficulties have progressed towards living ordinary lives in the community in many ways. For example:

- educational and employment opportunities;
- steps towards integration into the community through a continuing hospital closure programme;
- the growth of ordinary housing through the development of, for example, small group homes in the community;
- more flexible support services giving assistance at times and in ways to meet individual needs;
- the growth of self-advocacy (see p. 36).

Some questions about normalization

Wolfensberger argues that the ideas of normalization apply to any devalued group in society. Normalization emphasizes that the devalued group should adopt the culture and style of life of the dominant group (this process is sometimes called assimilation). However, while oppressed groups want to be valued as human beings, they will not necessarily wish to follow this approach. For example, for those black people who follow a traditional lifestyle, they should not be expected to change their eating habits or the way they dress to fit in with white people.

Susan Szivos, a lecturer and trainer at the University of Kent, argues that many good things have come from normalization but she is opposed to:

1 the assumption that assimilation is always a good thing;
2 the assumption that in order to be valued, disadvantaged groups should aspire to fulfil society's norms.

(Szivos, 1992, p. 128)

People in some oppressed groups do choose assimilation but it is an approach that can eventually destroy some of the strengths of the minority way of life. There are other strategies based on processes of self-help and conscious-ness-raising which acknowledge and celebrate differences and instil pride in them.

One strategy is to organize the oppressed group separately and ignore the wider society. Another is to encourage the group to organize itself collectively to change the values, attitudes and practice of the outside world.

Szivos gives as examples of groups asserting their value outside the main-stream culture, 'The positive assertion of sisterhood for the women's move-ment, of gayness for homosexuals and the proud slogan "Black is beautiful" for the black movement'(Szivos, 1992, p. 127).

Some view normalization as totally unacceptable. These people believe differences should be celebrated.

Szivos suggests that at a practical level, health and social care workers should not ask:
'Does this make my client conform to valued social norms?'

Instead they should ask whether the way of working improves:
'the self-concept of my client by acknowledging his or her right to feel positively about being different.'

(Szivos, 1992, p. 128)

Ideas and practice associated with self-advocacy and citizen advocacy have been greatly influenced by normalization. We will turn to these now.

Self-advocacy

Self-advocacy is people speaking and acting on their own behalf to present their case and take a more active role in their own community. The self-advocacy movement started in the United States and developed in the United Kingdom during the 1980s.

Statement by Liverpool self-advocacy group

'We need services that support us to become more independent. We have the right to a home of our own, a job, relationships and education but the services that we use must change to support us to have these rights. We do know that sometimes we need extra support to do some of the ordinary things in life, but don't we have a right to this support? We can and want to make decisions about our lives. Things need to be different in training centres and colleges and the people who are paid to work there and support us should give us more encour-agement. We need to give them training around what we need. This can be done simply by them listening to us and acting on what they hear.'

Two examples of organizations that encourage self-advocacy are:

People First

This organization, set up in 1984, encourages people with learning difficulties to take control of their own lives. Many self-advocacy groups are associated with it. The groups are made up of people with learning difficulties and are often based around training centres, hostels, and special schools.

Survivors Speak Out

This provides support for people who have experienced mental distress and associated health problems. They:

- give advice on how to set up and run a self-advocacy group;
- publish a self-advocacy action pack;
- provide skilled workers to give assistance and advice in the area where a group wishes to operate.

There is a long tradition of self-organization by disabled people and self-advocacy groups are a part of this.

Citizen advocacy

In 1966, delegates at a conference in the United States, concerned with cerebral palsy, looked at the question 'What will happen to my child when I'm gone?'

They decided that one answer might be that when no family is willing or able to protect a person's interests, those interests could continue to be protected by a 'citizen advocate'. A citizen advocate is an unpaid citizen who has no connection with the service provided to that person, thus avoiding any conflict of interest.

There are now many citizen advocacy offices in the USA, Canada and Australia, with an increasing number in the United Kingdom. Most of them are guided by principles developed by two key figures in the citizen advocacy movement, Wolf Wolfensberger and John O'Brien. You will recall that these men were also key figures in the development of ideas about normalization.

Citizen advocacy is offered by trained volunteers who work on behalf of people who are disabled and not in a position to defend their own rights as citizens. Citizen advocates are independent of those who provide direct services. They are introduced to an individual in need of support, often living in residential care, and get to know this person and their wishes. They become involved in helping to express the individual's day to day concerns.

Advocacy and the NHS&CC Act 1990

The concept of advocacy or authorized representation is missing from the 1990 Act. The guidance to the 1990 Act does encourage representation or advocacy where necessary, but it was not built into the actual legislation. Interestingly it was strongly built into the Disabled Persons Act 1986 but these were sections which the Government did not implement.

Advocacy systems are important for the following reasons:

- Any effective system of community care ought to incorporate more power for the user. An advocacy system is therefore an essential ingredient.
- Any attempt by health and welfare workers to promote anti-oppressive practice must incorporate using and working with a strong system of advocacy.
- Any way of working which sees disabled people as an oppressed group needs to incorporate ideas and strategies of self-advocacy.
- They help to prevent key processes of community care, such as assessment and care planning, from being dominated by the professionals involved.

Disability and social oppression

Over recent years normalization has represented a powerful and influential set of ideas for health and social care workers in the arena of community care. The discussion in this chapter should have helped to identify some of its strengths and some of its weaknesses. While normalization has developed specifically in relation to working with people with learning difficulties, the ideas can be applied to all groups connected with community care policies.

Another influential strand of ideas and practice for health and social care workers has come from the practice, theory, organization and writing of people with physical and sensory disabilities. A key concept in this context is 'disablism'.

The concepts of racism and sexism are more familiar than the concept of disablism. People are more used to discussing structures which oppress groups such as black people, working-class people and women. However, similar language can be used in relation to disabled people. Disablism means the ideas and practices which contribute to the oppression of disabled people. It covers the attitudes and actions which treat disabled people as second class.

As with racism, the processes of disablism can start early in our lives. Consider the negative images associated with characters in well-known children's stories such as Captain Hook in *Peter Pan* or Long John Silver in *Treasure Island*.

Two models can be used to explain how disability is regarded by society. A model is a simplified version of how things operate. It can help make sense of a complicated situation. The models are as follows:

- The 'traditional model' in which a disabled person is seen as having to adjust

to society. This model is sometimes called the medical model, the individual model or the personal tragedy model. Central aspects of it are:
- Disability is viewed as a 'tragic' situation.
- Individuals have to adapt to their impairment.
- Individuals have to adapt to fit into society.
- Individuals may be seen either as objects of pity or as heroes.
- The 'social oppression model' in which society is expected to adjust to the disabled person. It is a model put forward by a number of disabled persons' organizations and writers. Central aspects of it are:
  - Disabled people are an oppressed group, prevented from achieving their full potential by the structures of society.
  - Society 'disables' individuals by creating environmental obstacles and by its attitude to them.
  - Disabled people have the same range of needs and feelings as other people.
  - Society restricts disabled access to public transport, entertainment and public places.
  - Action within society needs to be taken to enable disabled people to play a full and equal part.

These two models simplify complex situations but if you are a disabled person or you care for a disabled person, you probably see your situation from one of these viewpoints. Most of us have probably been brought up with the first model, which is constantly reinforced by the media and by some charities.

The 'social oppression model' does not stress the restrictions created by impairments, but the restrictions created by a society geared to able-bodied people. It shows how society denies disabled people the means to do what they are capable of. The problem is not the impaired individual but the disabling society. This model emphasizes the need to identify and challenge the way social structures and institutions disable people with impairments.

Anti-oppressive practice for health and social care workers is about recognizing and challenging those disabling structures and working in a way that will enhance independence and increase the power of individuals and groups.

Language and disability

In a document on disability issues produced by the Central Council for Education and Training in Social Work, definitions of key words are suggested. These are given below and show how CCETSW has adopted the social oppression model of disability.

'Disability – the disadvantage or restriction caused by contemporary social organization which takes no or little account of people who have impairments and thus excludes them from activities.
Disabled person – someone who as a consequence of their impairment experiences social oppression of whatever kind.
Disablism – a form of social oppression or prejudice towards disabled people.'
(CCETSW, 1991, p. 16)

In his book, *The Politics of Disablement*, Michael Oliver argues that the traditional or personal tragedy theory of disability needs to be replaced by a social oppression theory of disability. He argues that impairments are not chance events happening to unfortunate people. Impairments often result from infectious diseases, poverty, or a lack of medical resources. There are 'structural' factors at work. In the United Kingdom a major factor is poverty and Townsend's study showed the links between poverty and disability (Townsend, 1979). There is also an increasing awareness of the 'structural' causes of heart attacks and strokes – relating to such factors as diet, stress, and lack of exercise.

Some key points which I would pick out from Oliver's study are:

- Research shows that disabled people receive poor services in terms of housing, employment, finance, transport and education (Oliver, 1990, p. 69).
- This is best explained in terms of a theory of social oppression.
- Many disabled people are women and some are black. They can suffer discrimination and oppression on account of gender and race as well as on account of being disabled.
- Taking a social oppression view of disability enables us to look at these issues and ask questions about the interweaving or interlinking of oppressions.

Disabled people or people with disabilities?

There is an on-going debate about the use of language and disability. I find the following contribution by Morris helpful:

> Disability refers to the oppression which people with physical, sensory or intellectual impairments, or those who are mental health system survivors, experience as a result of prejudicial attitudes and discriminatory actions. People are disabled by society's reaction to impairment: this is why the term 'disabled people' is used, rather than 'people with disabilities'. The latter really means 'people with impairments' whereas the disability movement prefers to use the more powerful term, 'disabled people', in order to place the emphasis on how society oppresses people with a whole range of impairments.
>
> (Morris, 1993, p. x)

Self-organization

There is a long history of self-organization by disabled people. In various ways they have challenged the medical and charitable view of disability. For example, the National League of the Blind formed as a registered trade union in 1899. In 1902 the League affiliated to the Trade Union Congress and became the first and only affiliated trade union consisting of disabled people. Another example was the formation in 1974 of the Union of Physically Impaired Against Segregation. In 1981 the British Council of Organizations of Disabled People (BCODP) was formed as a national coalition of organizations controlled by disabled people. In 1994 the BCODP had some 95 member organizations. These organizations of disabled people have campaigned for maximum independence in daily living activities and full integration into society with full control over their own lives. The organization of self-advocacy groups mentioned earlier in the chapter is therefore part of a long self-organizing tradition.

The British Deaf Association – an example of self-organization

One of the first campaigning organizations controlled by disabled people was the British Deaf Association founded in 1890. The British Deaf Association was set up as a self-help organization to promote the use of signing. This was partly in response to a congress of hearing educators in Milan in 1880 which voted to ban the use of sign languages in education throughout the world. These educators felt that deaf people should be trained and persuaded to speak and lip-read (a process called the 'oral method') so that they could play as full a part as possible in the hearing world.

Language is very important in giving a sense of identity. British Sign Language (BSL) is much used by deaf people, but it has had a struggle to survive. Peter Jackson writes on this in an interesting book on the history of the deaf community called *Britain's Deaf Heritage*:

> In order to suppress sign language, oral educators did everything they could to kill it. The cooperation of parents was sought, deaf teachers were refused employment, deaf children were told that using signs was bad and degrading. They were told that they would not grow up to be 'normal' people if they could not speak or lip-read; many children were told that if they went to deaf centres, they were failures for deaf clubs were dens of depravity where sign language flourished.
>
> (Jackson, 1990, p. 347)

The use of the word 'normal' raises interesting issues related to the earlier discussion of normalization. Here is a group with their own distinctive language, their own jokes and humour indicating the value of celebrating difference rather than struggling to be like the majority.

Independent living

In the United States during the 1960s disability was an issue within the Civil Rights movement. Discrimination was identified as a major issue:

- against black people;
- against women;
- against disabled people.

The links between oppressed groups seem to have been made more clearly in the United States than in the United Kingdom.

In the United States this movement of disabled people has sometimes been called the Independent Living Movement. One aspect of this was disabled people taking service provision into their own hands and one result was the first Centre For Independent Living in Berkeley, California, in 1972. By 1983 there were 135 such centres in the United States. The Independent Living Movement wishes to 'demedicalize' disability and not label disabled people as 'sick'. The movement has been slower to develop in the United Kingdom, but there are examples such as the Derbyshire Centre For Integrated Living and the Hampshire Centre For Independent Living.

Derbyshire Centre For Integrated Living

The Derbyshire Centre For Integrated Living was set up in the early 1980s. It is run and managed by disabled people for disabled people and its mission is 'to secure independent, integrated living opportunities for disabled people in order to promote their full participation in the mainstream of economic life in Derbyshire'. The centre offers a range of services such as peer counselling, help and information, and a wheelchair repair and maintenance scheme.

The setting up by the government of the Independent Living Fund (ILF) in 1988 in the U.K. encouraged independent living in the following ways:

- A disabled person would apply and be assessed.
- If they satisfied the criteria, they would be given a regular grant which would enable them to employ people who could assist them to live independently.
- The fund thus gave disabled people control over their own carers. They could employ them and tell them what to do. This was a very different relationship to the disabled person having to fit into the organization of the local home care and nursing service.
- Through such means power was shifted to the disabled person.

The new fund gave a vision of how user-led and user-controlled care packages could be set up to meet the real needs of disabled people. Part of the community care package of the early 1990s involved severely restricting the role of the Independent Living Fund. The ILF was closed in March 1993 by the government. By then 21,500 severely disabled users were receiving regular payments to enable them to buy in personal care and domestic assistance. It was replaced by two new trusts:

1 The Independent Living (Extension) Fund was registered as a charitable trust in order to continue payments to existing claimants.
2 The Independent Living (1993) Fund was established for new claimants. It provides a top-up to council services and is resourced to accept 1,500 new applicants of working age a year. It excludes pensioners. Applicants need to show that without help they would have to go into residential care.

There was a great deal of anger among disabled people about the loss of the Independent Living Fund in its original form as it gave the possibility of greater self-control and independence for disabled people.

A*ctivity* ▬▬▬▬▬▬▬▬▬▬▬▬▬▬▬▬▬▬▬▬▬▬▬▬

At the end of Chapter 1 it was suggested that you should have a look at your local Community Care Plan. It would be useful to look at it again in the light of the discussion in this chapter. Particular points to look out for would be:

• Information about normalization, ordinary life ideas, self-advocacy, citizen advocacy or advocacy;
• Ways in which the plan for care of disabled people has been influenced by the 'social oppression model' or ideas of 'independent living'.

Key questions

1 What is normalization?
2 Outline some strengths and weaknesses of normalization.
3 Outline the differences between self-advocacy and citizen advocacy.
4 Outline two models of disability.
5 In what ways do the models influence how we think about and work with disabled people?
6 What vision of community care did the Independent Living Fund offer?

Further reading

Brown, H. and Smith, H. *Normalisation,* Routledge and Oliver, London, 1992.
Oliver, M. *The Politics of Disablement,* Macmillan, 1990.
Read, J. and Wallcroft, J. *Guidelines on Advocacy for Mental Health Workers,* Mind/ Unison, 1994. The trade union, Unison, and the voluntary organization, MIND, have cooperated to draw up advocacy guidelines for health and social care workers. Both organizations are anxious that workers adopt a positive rather than a negative approach to advocacy.
Begum, N., Hill, M. and Stevens, A. *Reflections,* CCETSW, London, 1994. This is written by black, disabled peple about their lives and community care. It is also relevant to the next chapter.

4

Race, social divisions and community care

Preview

This chapter focuses on:

○ race as an example of a social division in relation to community care;
○ the lack of attention paid to race in government legislation and in reports;
○ the death of Beverley Lewis as an example of a breakdown in community care;
○ the inter-linking of race with other social divisions.

Race and community care

Chapter 2 introduced the categorization of social divisions as gender, class, sexual orientation, disability, age and race. All services should be sensitive to existing social divisions. The practice of workers (whether from health services or social services, the voluntary or the private sector) needs to take account of those divisions and try to actively counter them. In order to do this effectively, workers need to understand oppression and how it is structurally determined. Chapter 2 included a discussion of social divisions in relation to carers. Chapter 3 covered disability and oppression. In a book of this size it is not possible to cover all the social divisions in any detail. This chapter will focus on 'race' in the context of community care. The coverage of race and disability (Chapter 3) should be seen as illustrative.

Language and race

As similar types of discrimination are faced by people of Asian, Afro/Caribbean and Chinese origin, they are often collectively described as 'black'. This term is political rather than analytical and is used to express the common experience of racism by these groups.

However, some members of these groups object to the use of the word 'black' in this way. They would rather emphasize the diversity of race and prefer to use more specific terms such as 'Asian', 'Chinese' or 'Afro/Caribbean'.

Some words are offensive and should not be used. Other words may be more acceptable to one person or group than another. It is important to note that there are important on-going debates about language in the discussion of race. Health and social care workers need to be sensitive to what language is appropriate to different groups and situations.

This book follows the King's Fund Centre in using the descriptive phrase, 'black communities'. This refers to people from racial or other minorities who may be disadvantaged because of their racial backgrounds. 'It is accepted that there is not one word that embraces or is embraced by all members of minority racial groups in this country. When the term ethnic minority is used, it will be as a result of using quoted material.'

(Wilson, 1993, p. v)

Skellington (1992) has summarized some useful evidence illustrating the discrimination and oppression of black communities in society. Many examples of inequalities are given but some key points made are that:

- Black communities suffer from racial harassment and racial violence;
- Black communities are more at risk of high unemployment, low pay, shift work and poor social security rights;
- Black communities suffer from an inequality of access to and provision of housing.

Race Relations Act 1976

This Act makes illegal discrimination on the grounds of race, colour, nationality and ethnic origin. Section 71 of the Act requires local authorities to ensure that their functions are carried out with due regard to the need to eliminate unlawful racial discrimination; and to promote equality of opportunity, and good relations between people of different racial groups. Local authorities should also ensure that services provided are non-discriminatory. Under the Act, positive action is allowed in order to encourage members of a particular group to participate if they have been under represented, or to ensure the welfare of a particular group. The 1976 Act also established the Commission for Racial Equality which carries out research, provides information and has the power to investigate organizations' practices and procedures.

Many studies have shown that black communities receive poor or inappropriate services from the National Health Service. In her book, *Black Health: A Political Issue*, Torkington summarized some of the issues:

- there is poor health provision for elders in black communities;
- low priority is given to screening for diabetes and high blood pressure in health and community centres;
- there is meagre availability of translation and interpreting services;
- low priority is given to health promotion and prevention;
- there is ignorance amongst health professionals about cultural matters such as diet;
- in senior management positions in the NHS there is poor representation of people from black communities;
- there is racism within mental health services and mental health treatment.

(cited in Amin, 1992, p. 24)

Some recognition of these issues was given by government in 1993 with the launching of the NHS Ethnic Health Unit. Based in Leeds, the role of the unit is to secure full benefit for black communities from the NHS. The team will try to address the obstacles and discrimination that people from black communities face when using the health services.

Overt and covert discrimination

Overt discrimination

This occurs when people from ethnic minority groups are treated in an obviously second-class way. In extreme forms, it includes assaults and threats and may be shown through the use of offensive and objectionable language. Intolerance or hostility may be shown through actions and behaviour. It may be clearly put across that the organization's or white staff's way of doing things (for example, in relation to diet or food preparation) is superior to the ideas of black communities.

Covert discrimination

This type of discrimination is more hidden and subtle. For example, no one may have thought of the need for a translation service or of the need to take account of dietary or religious needs. In this sort of way the organization automatically disadvantages black people. This is sometimes called 'institutional racism'.

The experiences of poor housing, poor health care, lack of education, and poorer employment opportunities result in black people as a group having greater needs. An extra effort is needed from services to counter the greater need. The next section will look at the extent to which the varied reports and legislation concerned with community care (outlined in Chapter 1) have acknowledged that greater need.

Race, reports and legislation

Recent government reports and legislation have made relatively little reference to issues of race.

The *House of Commons Social Services Report on Community Care* (1985) had 101 recommendations. Only one of these referred to the needs of black communities. This was:

> We recommend that those responsible for the delivery of services to mentally disabled adults take steps to ensure that any particular needs of ethnic minority people are met and that the services in fact reach all the community for whom they are intended.
>
> (Recommendation 30)

Significantly, the committee that produced this report received no evidence that mental health and disability services 'were either provided or needed on a different basis' (para 160).

Chapter 1 (page 3) noted the powerful critique of community care policies contained in the 1986 Audit Commission Report, *'Making A Reality of*

Community Care'. However, this was an example of a colour-blind approach to racism in that it did not even acknowledge that there was an issue.

A 'colour-blind' approach

A colour-blind service is one that is designed and delivered in the same way for all the population. It is assumed that the service will be equally accessible and equally appropriate for all those who may have a need for it. It ignores the fact that we live in a multiracial society in which services should be adapted for particular needs.

The Griffiths Report of 1988 devotes just one paragraph to the topic of race:

> Both policy and action need to respond to the multi-racial nature of British society. The emphasis on the responsibility of the social services authority to assess need, and arrange appropriate packages of services for individuals *within their own situations*, should help to ensure that the different needs of people with different cultural back-grounds are properly considered. All staff involved will need to be trained to develop the appropriate knowledge and skill to do this successfully.
>
> (p. 26)

In the 1989 White Paper, *Caring For People*, there are even fewer words:

> The Government recognizes that people from different cultural backgrounds may have particular care needs and problems. Minority communities may have different concepts of community care and it is important that service providers are sensitive to these variations. Good community care will take account of the circumstances of minority communities and will be planned in consultation with them.
>
> (Para 2.9)

The White Paper also says that decisions on service provision have to take account of what is 'available and affordable'(DoH, 1989, p. 20). This is especially relevant to black communities because sometimes different and extra provision is essential. This necessarily costs money.

The NHS and Community Care Act 1990 makes no reference to race or culture within those sections of the 1990 Act which relate to community care. This omission contrasts with the Children Act 1989 which requires service providers to be sensitive to a child's race and culture.

It will be clear that the coverage of race has been very limited in the early documents and non-existent in the actual legislation. Though there has been some coverage in later guidance documents this has not been great.

Workers in health and social care need to acknowledge the very limited coverage of race and cultural issues within these reports and policies and work out anti-discriminatory and anti-oppressive methods of practice.

Sometimes, few of the standard services are suitable for the black communities. For instance:

• Meals on wheels provision or food provided in day care or residential homes which makes no allowance for the diets of different communities and cultures.
• Residential homes which in their organization and provision make no allowance for the religious and prayer needs of some residents.

- Services which are only provided for both men and women together. (Men and women from some communities may feel uncomfortable eating together or mixing together freely.)

The colour-blind approach of 'we offer the same services to everyone' is inherently discriminatory. Provision really has to be 'needs-led' to be at all sensitive to people from black communities. Where services do not 'fit' there is a tendency to build up a myth that 'they look after their own'.

They look after their own

'"They care for their own" is a myth, and an unfair assumption to make, because it is used as a buffer by the Social Services Departments against making any necessary changes to the existing services and expanding the level of service provision. The important question here is not whether extended family structures exist, but whether black elders are receiving different forms of care from the welfare state, according to their requirements, irrespective of the nature of the family structure. The maintenance and reproduction of the myth that "they look after their own" has allowed Social Services Departments to evade their responsibility of providing care – a cost effective evasion because it saves resources; but does not require a change in the pattern of resource distribution; and it keeps the existing services intact.'

(Patel, 1990, p. 31)

Potential for change

Blakemore and Boneham (1994) stress that the situation of elders from black communities has not been high on the agenda of policy makers in health and social services or of social research.

Our knowledge of issues and problems is therefore somewhat limited and services have neglected this group of users.

The authors suggest that the community care changes do present some possibilities for positive change. For example:

- The contracting out of services may make it easier to provide meals for older Asians with differing dietary needs.
- The funding arrangements and the emphasis on user choice may mean that the chances of 'ethnically sensitive' residential accommodation could improve.
- Purchasing arrangements could stimulate a flow of funds into services run by voluntary organizations for older black and Asian people.

(Blakemore and Boneham, 1994, pp. 134–5)

Strategies and approaches towards provision for black elders vary a good deal between areas. In the box below is a checklist on health services for black elders. You could use the checklist to assess actual services provided in your own area.

Checklist of services for black elderly people

- Are there joint health care planning teams for the development of policy and service planning for elderly people which include black community organizations?
- Are there procedures to ensure that community care plans include reference to:
  - how service provision will aim to meet the needs of black elderly people and their carers?
  - arrangements for consulting these service users and their carers?
- Are there procedures to ensure effective discharge planning for elderly people which include arrangements for multidisciplinary liaison between hospital and commmunity health care teams and appropriate community organizations.
- Are there arrangements to monitor the satisfaction of black patients and their carers with discharge assessments and with post-discharge arrangements?
- Are there procedures for the ethnic monitoring of emergency readmission rates for elderly patients?
- Are there arrangements with the Social Services Department to enable review of the service provision in day hospitals and centres to ensure the appropriate placement of black elderly people?
- Are there arrangements for liaison with sheltered housing schemes for people from these populations?
- Are there arrangements to enable:
  - hearing tests and speech therapy to be conducted in community languages?
  - eye tests to be conducted using symbols or community languages?

(Slightly adapted from Gunaratnam Y. 1993, Checklist: Health & Race, London: King's Fund Centre. p26/27).

Key principles for anti-racist practice

Developing an anti-racist practice in the area of community care is an ambitious goal but there are certain key principles that should be borne in mind at all times if this is to be achieved.

Countering overt and covert racism
Overt and covert (or institutional) racism within health and social care organizations should be actively countered.

Promoting self-help in black communities
Black communities have a long history of providing care services for their own members and it is useful to find out about their knowledge and experience. Self-help is an important area for workers to understand and small voluntary organizations can be very helpful. Phaure writes:

'An appreciation of the work performed by black self-help projects is entirely absent from the Government's literature on community care' (1991, p. 8).

Challenging common myths
A very common myth in the field of caring in black communities is that 'they

look after their own'. This is sometimes true but it should never be assumed and presented as a justification for not providing a service.

Countering racist intervention

Black communities usually receive more attention from the controlling aspects of the welfare state and less attention and provision from the providing aspects (Skellington, p. 87).

The box below on racism and mental health gives some specific areas in which this is true. Ways in which racism may be operating within agency structures need to be identified, acknowledged and removed.

Racism and mental health

'Studies over the past 20 years show that black people are more likely than white to be:

- removed by police to a place of safety under section 136 of the Mental Health Act 1983;
- retained in hospital under sections 2, 3, and 4 of the Mental Health Act;
- diagnosed as suffering from schizophrenia or another form of psychotic illness;
- detained in locked wards of psychiatric hospitals;
- given higher dosages of medication.'

(MIND, 1993, p. 1)

Promoting take-up of services

In terms of the 'providing' aspects of the welfare state, black communities may receive a poorer service than white communities. For example, black people in an area may receive fewer mobile meals or less home care provision than their proportion of the population would suggest was appropriate. Positive action is needed to improve the low take-up of some services. Sometimes separate provision for black communities may be the most appropriate way forward.

Delivering appropriate community care

Black communities have a right to appropriate community care and it should never be seen as or portrayed as a special privilege. This may mean a meals service which makes special provision for dietary needs or a home care service which particularly recruits workers from the community where there is a need for care.

Action programme

In June, 1993, the government launched an eighteen-month programme of action to improve mental health services for black communities. The intention of the programme was to keep race on the agenda by working with professionals and people in the community. This was a relatively small initiative but it indicated that there was an acknowledgement of the issue by government.

Listening to black users

Care workers should make an effort to learn from black users about their needs and how they wish to be treated. One study of district nurses showed that they had made little attempt to learn from older black and Asian patients (Cameron et al. 1989).

Understanding the impact of other social divisions

While concentrating on anti-racist policies other issues can be forgotten. For example, an approach which focuses solely on race could neglect some of the divisions and differences between the older members of black and ethnic communities. It is important for carers not to narrow their vision in this way.

A real black woman who fell through the net of community care was Beverley Lewis. Her situation is given here as an example in order to:

- emphasize the necessity for services to be sensitive to the needs of black communities.
- draw out the way in which the impact of social divisions such as disability, race and gender may be inter-related.

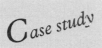

Beverley Lewis

Beverley Lewis was born with several impairments – visual and hearing impairment, some physical impairment and severe learning difficulty. She died in February, 1989, aged 23 in Gloucester. She had lived with her black, Afro-Caribbean family who, until her parents separated, consisted of her mother and father and five brothers and sisters.

When Beverley died her weight was 3 stone 13lbs and her height was 5 feet. She had lived in very poor surroundings and was found naked on a settee surrounded by newspapers. Over the years prior to her death her mother had looked after her. However the mother's mental health had been deteriorating and on Beverley's death she was diagnosed schizophrenic.

Beverley had been known to the Health Authority from 1966 until she died and to the Social Services Department since 1970. She had been excluded from her school at the age of 10 due to aggressive behaviour on the school bus. At the inquest the coroner criticized the GP who had never seen Beverley, believing social services were monitoring her, and the social worker who had seen her only seven times in four years.

This situation raises some key issues in relation to the failings of community care, race and also the inter-twining of different dimensions of oppression. Some questions posed by this situation are:

1   Black people often report receiving insensitive and inadequate services. Here were two black women dropping through the net of health and welfare provision. Was race a factor?

2   Beverley was looked after by her mother who was increasingly in need of care herself. Could more have been done to support the mother in her role as carer? Is it possible that both of them would have received more attention if the carer had been the father?

3   Services for disabled people generally have been given a low priority in terms of health and social services provision. Beverley was a disabled person and her mother had also become disabled by mental health problems. Was the situa-

tion in any way a result of the low priority which has generally been given to disability by Social Services Departments?

4   It will have become clear that with Beverley Lewis the questions raised have not simply been about community care and race. There are issues of disability and gender here as well. Issues of social divisions, oppression and community care interlink and intertwine.

The inter-linking of oppression

The title of a book about people with learning difficulties from black and ethnic minority communities is *Double Discrimination* (Baxter, C. et al. 1990). The point that the authors are making with the title is that:

- there is a stigma attached to having a learning difficulty;
- being black as well means a double disadvantage in terms of how you are treated by society.

Women who are old are sometimes described as suffering the 'double jeopardy' of age and gender. They may be treated poorly on account of their age and their gender. Similarly black, older women could be described as suffering the 'triple jeopardy' of age, gender and race.

We are confronted here with the issue of how the different social divisions relate to one another. Is there one division or power relationship (for example: race, class or gender) which is the dominant or main division? Alternatively, is there a gradation or hierarchy of divisions with some (for example: race, class and gender) being seen as more important and influential than others (for example: age, disability and sexual orientation)?

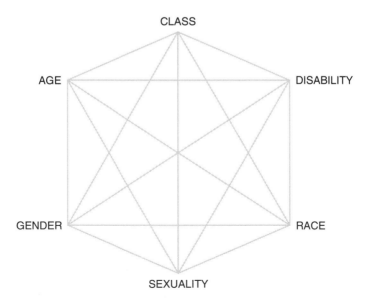

Figure 4.1: A model of some of the social divisions that affect people's lives (Williams, 1992, p. 214).

In Figure 4.1 Williams suggests a model of some of the obvious divisions that affect people's lives.

Clearly this is not a hierarchy of divisions where one division is seen as more important than others. Williams argues that we can see this as a series of lines which represent different social relations of power. It could be imagined as three-dimensional or, more imaginatively,

'as one of those many-mirrored spherical lights which revolves above dance floors, catching and throwing the reflections of the room and those individuals and groups within in a constantly shifting but nevertheless patterned way'.

(Williams, 1992, p. 214)

The model helps us to appreciate that any individual user of health and social care services will have needs and will make choices which are influenced by divisions and differences. The many mirrors of the model show that social divisions impact on individuals and groups in varying ways at differing times and situations. In the above discussion of Beverley Lewis, divisions of disability, race, and gender were especially drawn out.

The model also helps us to understand the impact of more than one division on individuals and groups. This relates to the 'double jeopardy' and 'triple jeopardy' mentioned earlier. Williams writes,

'Race, class and gender have a compounding effect on the experiences and life chances of a black working class woman.'

(Williams, 1992, p. 215)

*A*ctivity

If you are working in a health or welfare organization or you have some contact with one, try to obtain a copy of its equal opportunities policy. Study it and consider what you feel is good about it? How do you feel it might be improved? Try to make some connections between it and issues of community care.

Key questions

1 Outline the coverage of race in the documents leading up to the NHS&CC Act 1990.
2 What key principles would you identify for anti-racist practice?
3 In what ways can you see inter-linking of oppressions in relation to community care?

Further reading

Williams, A. *Caring For People. . . Caring For Profit,* Voluntary Service Council, London, 1992. A detailed critique of the community care changes in relation to race.
Baxter, C., Poona, K., Ward, L. and Nadirshaw, Z. *Double Discrimination,* King's Fund Centre and Commission for Racial Equality, London, 1990. A lively and interesting look at the issues and services for people with learning difficulties from black and ethnic minority communities.
Webb, R. and Tossell, D. *Social Issues For Carers,* Edward Arnold, London, 1991. A book which looks at the structural inequalities of class, race, gender, disability, age and sexual orientation in the context of carers and community care.

5

Care management and assessment

Preview

This chapter considers two key linked issues concerned with community care:

○ care/case management;
○ assessing need.

Care/case management

An important element of the White Paper, *Caring For People* was the approval given to case management. Where needs are complex or involve significant expense then:

> . . . the Government sees considerable merit in nominating a 'case manager' to take responsibility for ensuring that individuals' needs are regularly reviewed, resources are managed effectively and that each service user has a single point of contact.
>
> (DoH, 1989b, p. 21)

The White Paper talked about 'case' management. Later government publications and much of the recent literature now refer to 'care' management, which is the term used by this book. It is important to realize that both terms may be used.

There is no single model of care management and there are different ways of arranging and carrying it out. Very often, the effectiveness of community care depends on the efficiency of care management. This raises the issue of whether the present system can deliver good services or whether a structural reorganization of services is needed. First, it is useful to have some detail of the background influences on care management.

Background to care management in the UK

There have been a number of influences on the development of care management in the U.K. Emphasis here will be given to:

• influences from North America;
• the idea of the keyworker;
• individual programme planning;

- the Kent Community Care Scheme;
- the Care in the community pilot projects;

Care management in North America

The language of care management comes from the United States. Although in the United Kingdom it is sometimes considered that services are badly coordinated, fragmented and patchy, it has been worse in the United States. From the United States there are over three decades of experience and many of the ideas and practice of care management have come from there. Experience in the US has produced a variety of models of what care management has been and might be.

From Canada comes the idea of service brokerage. This approach to care management is commonly thought to have had its origins in the determination of the Independent Living Movement in Canada to help people with severe physical impairments to live independent lives in the community. It has been defined by the Norah Fry Research Centre, University of Bristol, as having the following elements:

- Service brokers are independent of all the agencies who provide services.
- The role of the broker is to help clients decide what support they need. Then they design and negotiate a package of services from the most appropriate source, acting as a guide through the system.
- The brokers are solely accountable to the people with learning difficulties and their carers and friends in the community.

(Harrison and Means, 1993, p. 118)

Care management in the UK does not have as long a history as it does in North America. The ideas behind its development have been influenced by experience in the United States but also by some developments in the UK.

The idea of the keyworker

The idea of the 'keyworker' has been around for a number of years. Keyworkers were originally used to deal with situations that involved both residential and fieldwork services. This involvement often led to confusion about who was doing what. The keyworker's role was to provide a central point for communication. Anyone else involved in the situation would be able to report to keyworkers about problems, or obtain information from them. The keyworker could be from either the residential or the fieldwork sector, but was supposed to ensure that the person in residential care did not slip through the net of care with nobody really taking a close interest. The role of the keyworker was therefore over and above the job of residential or field social worker.

The idea of a keyworker has been particularly applied to residential care, especially the residential care of children, but it has also been applied to work in the community.

It is hard to be sure of the relationship between 'keyworker' and 'care manager'. The Policy Guidance distinguishes between the two as follows:

- The key worker carries the main service-providing role.
- Care managers, on the other hand, have been separated from service provision.
- The range of responsibilities carried by care managers and the fact that they are not involved in direct service delivery distinguishes their role from that of key workers.
- It will not be possible for care managers to be assessors as well as providers. As care managers are not seen as providers or service deliverers they could not be keyworkers.

(DoH, 1990a, p. 25)

Individual programme planning

This is a way of working with people with learning difficulties that has become more widely used in recent years.

Individual Programme Plans (IPPs) operate on the idea of individually tailored services by a team of professionals in consultation with the user and carers. The plans should be written down, making clear everyone's contribution and should be regularly reviewed.

Central to IPPs is a meeting at which the main decisions are made. Usually this meeting is attended by the user, their relatives and/or an advocate, as well as direct care staff and managers. Opportunities are provided for the user and their family to participate in the meeting as much as possible.

The example of the Kent Community Care Scheme

From the late 1970s onwards Kent Social Services experimented with care management and this was followed by other pilot projects around the country. The first project in Kent was the Thanet Community Care project. It was a collaborative venture with the Personal Social Services Research Unit (PSSRU) at the University of Kent. In their write-up of it Challis and Davies argue that care management is a response to four interconnected problems:

(a) A virtual absence of resource coordination;
(b) The difficulty of interweaving statutory and informal care;
(c) The relative neglect of older people in social work;
(d) The problems of accountability.

(Challis and Davies, 1986, p. 2–8)

Care management was seen as a way of trying to tackle these four problems. The Kent scheme targeted a group of older people who would normally have been appropriate for residential care. Instead of offering them residential care, a package of care in the community was put together. The packages cost up to two-thirds of the cost of residential care. A specialist team of workers, with relatively small caseloads managed the scheme. The team managed the budget themselves. This meant that they were able to use the money flexibly and change their plans easily as the situation changed.

The box below contains Hunter's summary of the main results of this pilot project:

Summary of results of Kent Pilot Project

The project succeeded in:

- halving the probability of death within one year;
- halving the probability of admission to long-term care;
- doubling the probability of continuing to live at home;
- achieving large favourable differences in the probabilities of death, admission to institutions, and remaining at home over three years;
- improving surviving clients' own perceptions of their well-being;
- improving the quality of their care;
- reducing average costs of social services departments without imposing extra costs on the National Health Service;
- relieving informal carers of important burdens during clients' lives and reduced costs to them;
- reducing the cost to society of surviving clients.

(Hunter, 1988, p. 22)

It is clear from the White Paper that the Kent scheme and other pilot schemes influenced the Government's thinking about how community care should be organized across the country as a whole.

Care in the community pilot projects

In 1983 the then Department of Health and Social Security (DHSS) launched a 'care in the community' initiative. This involved funding 28 projects for three years. The projects were innovatory projects involving community care arrangements for people in long-stay hospitals (Renshaw et al. 1988). The Personal Social Services Research Unit (PSSRU) at the University of Kent was given the role of promoting, monitoring and evaluating the projects.

One of the conditions for the DHSS programme funding of projects was that some form of care management procedures should be established for people leaving hospitals. The projects showed how complicated it was to bring about a careful and sensitive transfer of vulnerable people from long-stay institutions into community settings. These projects, and the PSSRU evaluation and monitoring of them, no doubt played some part in the appearance of the care management recommendations within the White Paper of 1989.

This brief background aims to show that there are various strands of influence which lead into our current understanding of care management. There are strands coming from the experience of people in North America and the United Kingdom as well as various models of care management.

The Department of Health model of care management

In a useful Department of Health publication called *Care Management and Assessment: Practitioners' Guide*, it says that, 'Care management is the process of tailoring services to individual needs (DoH, 1991a, p. 9). The Guide suggests seven core tasks involved in arranging care for someone in need. These are shown in the box below:

The core tasks of care management

There can be said to be seven core tasks of care management. These are:

1 publishing information;
2 determining the level of assessment;
3 assessing need;
4 care planning;
5 implementing the care plan;
6 monitoring;
7 reviewing.

Figure 5.1, taken from the guidance, shows how care management can be seen as a cyclical process through which needs are assessed, services are delivered in response to identified needs and needs are then re-assessed, resulting in a possibility of a changed service response.

A source of some confusion – the care management and the care programme approach

Alongside the care management approach the Department of Health has required District Health Authorities to develop the Care Programme Approach (CPA) for people with a severe mental illness (people referred to specialist psychiatric services).

The care programme approach was implemented in April, 1991. This approach requires District Health Authorities, in collaboration with Social Services Departments, to design and put into practice arrangements for treating a user in the community and ensuring that they receive the necessary care.

Care management and CPA are very similar and this has led to some confusion. They are similar in that they both include the same core tasks of assessment, planning, implementation and review.

Care management and CPA are different in that:

- CPA uses keyworkers rather than care managers;
- CPA is health led while Care Management is local authority led.

A research study on CPA conducted for and published by the Department of Health has commented:

The existence of two different initiatives aimed at planning and managing care in the community has caused some confusion amongst professionals involved in the mental health area.

(North et al., 1993, p. 18)

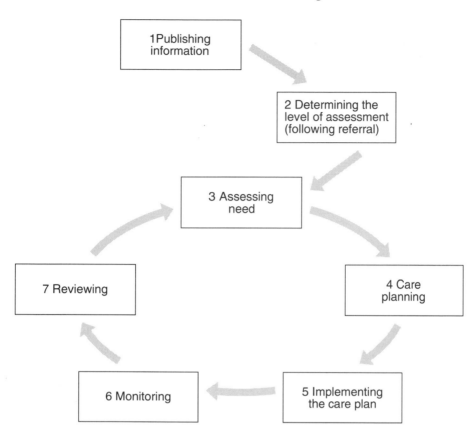

Figure 5.1: The process of care management (DoH, 1991a, p. 10).

An example of care management – Mr Lafferty

This study of Jim Lafferty illustrates the seven tasks of care management. It is a fictional case but it is based on the types of situation which social workers and care managers deal with. It shows:

- the publishing of information through the leaflet given by the GP;
- a Social Services team leader determining the level of assessment;
- a social worker (or care manager) coordinating the assessment of need, negotiating the care plan and ensuring the care plan is implemented;
- a social worker monitoring the situation and deciding on a review when the situation deteriorates.

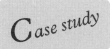

Jim Lafferty

Jim Lafferty used to work on the docks. He is now 88 years old. His wife died in July, 1992. Since then he has lived alone in a privately-owned terraced property. He suffers from arthritis and has a hearing impairment.

A few months ago he started to become very confused at times and rather uncooperative. Of major concern was his wandering at night and in the early mornings. Jim was returned home by the police on a few occasions and could give no indication of where he had been.

Jim has a very supportive and concerned family: two daughters (Maureen and Jane) and one son (Harold). They took their concern to Jim's GP who felt that Jim should be in a residential home. He gave them a leaflet about assessments by Social Services and rang the local office to tell them of his concerns and his view.

Different levels of assessment

Not everyone will receive a full assessment. In reality most authorities seem to have two levels of assessment:

- A simple assessment where there is a straight-forward request and need and is dealt with quickly. Examples would be assessment for a bus pass or a disabled persons' car badge. The assessment may well be made by a receptionist or a member of the administrative staff.
- A comprehensive assessment where priority should be given to those whose impairment of functioning places their continued independent living in the community at risk. No one should be admitted to residential care without a prior comprehensive assessment of their needs. Authorities need to be selective because of the time-consuming nature of these assessments.

The team leader within the local Social Services office considered the information she had and set it against the department's agreed policy on categories of need. She was aware of the four categories of need which the department had agreed on and now implemented as a policy (each authority has worked out its own categories of need, sometimes called eligibility criteria). In this department the four categories of need can be summarized as follows:

- **Category 1, High Priority**: This is where an emergency or crisis point has been reached.
- **Category 2, Medium Priority**: This is where a high level of need is suspected.
- **Category 3, Low Priority**: Needs appear to exist and a response from the Department would be appropriate.
- **Category 4, Non Priority**: Help may be desirable but it is not essential that it comes from Social Services.

The department had only been responding to Priorities 1 and 2 as it has not had the resources to respond to Priorities 3 and 4. The team leader thought that the situation seemed to fit into Priority 2 and decided that a comprehensive assessment was needed. She gave the job of coordinating this assessment to a social worker called Sharma. (In some authorities the social worker might be called a care manager.) The Department had designed a lengthy form to be filled in for comprehensive assessments. Sharma visited Jim and tried to explain her role and get to know him a bit. She spoke to the GP over the phone and met with one of the daughters. She visited Jim twice more, the second time with the home care organizer.

In her three visits to Jim, Sharma tried to get a view of his life and what he wants to do. During the course of her three visits, and information from others, she was able to fill in the assessment document. On her third visit she took the form with her and completed the sections she had not been able to fill in up to that point.

Sharma assessed that Jim wished to stay in his own home and that this would be possible with some extra support. It was the GP who felt that residential care was necessary. The family was worried, but Sharma felt that they wanted what was best for their father and that they would do what they could to help.

Uncertain or conflicting needs

In practice, obtaining an agreement about someone's needs may be very complicated. There may be different views and perceptions between users, carers and other care agencies. In the Department of Health's *Practitioners' Guide* it says that, 'although the ideal is to achieve consensus, the users' views should carry the most weight' (DoH, 1991a, p. 53).

There can be real dilemmas when users cannot clearly express their wishes and needs. This could be, for example, where they are confused or suffer from dementia. The worker will then have to make some judgement about their wishes and needs which can be difficult.

A problem for health and social care workers is that quite often the needs of the carer(s) and the user are in conflict with each other. The 1986 Disabled Persons' Act legislation was much stronger in offering separate assessments to carers and users. The Practitioners' Guide says:

'Where there is significant disagreement between users and carers, it may be appropriate to offer the carers the opportunity of a separate assessment of their needs' (DoH, 1991a, p. 53).

Skill and tact can be involved in arranging for the user and the carer to be interviewed separately.

Assessment is one of the seven tasks of care management. It is therefore part of a process and the next stage is working out a care plan. Sharma has discussions with various people and pulls together a package of care which she feels could support Jim throughout the week. Getting appropriate support throughout the week takes quite a lot of phone calls and negotiation. A summary of the final plan is given on page 62.

Sharma supplies everyone concerned with a copy of the plan. As part of her overall assessment Sharma has to do an assessment of Jim's financial situation. As a result Jim has to make a contribution to the cost of his mobile meals, the home care service and the day care service.

Sharma keeps in touch with the home care worker and the home care organizer as a way of monitoring the situation. The care plan works quite well for about six months.

Monday	8–9 home care	day centre 9.30–3.30 4–5 home care	daughter – evening meal son – puts to bed
Tuesday	8–9 home care	meals on wheels home care 12–12.30 & 3–4 daughter pops in through day	daughter – evening meal son – puts to bed
Wednesday	8–9 home care	day centre 9.30–3.30 4–5 home care	daughter – evening meal son – puts to bed
Thursday	8–9 home care	meals on wheels home care 12–12.30 & 3–4 daughter pops in through day	daughter – evening meal son – puts to bed
Friday	8–9 home care	day centre 9.30–3.30 4–5 home care	daughter – evening meal son – puts to bed
Saturday	family support	meals on wheels 1 hour home care & family support	family support
Sunday	family support	meals on wheels 1 hour home care & family support	family support

The role and skills of a home care worker

Role

Assessment is a continuous process. The home care worker will be in the best situation to see how the care plan is working out and be able to pass this information back to Sharma. The home care worker needs to make clear to Jim and the family that information about the situation will be passed on to the home care organizer and to Sharma. Thus the home care worker has an important role in continuing to assess the situation and in monitoring it.

Skills

The skills of the home care worker needed in this situation will include:

- performing the agreed tasks satisfactorily;
- not always doing jobs for Jim but, where possible, doing them with him;
- being open and honest about the role being taken in helping to monitor the situation;

- relating to different people involved;
- being clear about what information might be passed on to the organizer and to Sharma;
- being a source of information to Jim and his family about the whole care management process;
- having enough knowledge of the welfare benefits system to know whether Jim and his family need further advice in this area.

> After six months the situation deteriorates and Sharma notices that it is one daughter, Maureen, who seems to carry the extra load. Jim has become more confused and has wandered in the evenings/mornings on several occasions. Sharma feels he really requires someone to stay overnight with him.
>
> As far as Sharma is able to judge Jim still wants to stay at home. Maureen is spending more time in the evenings with Jim and staying overnight sometimes. Sharma feels Maureen is stretched to the limit. She feels more coverage (and probably overnight care) has now to be built into the care plan.
>
> It is time to review the situation. Some options are:
>
> - Putting in overnight care from a private agency. This is costly.
> - Respite care in a nearby local authority home. This could be perhaps one week every two months or one week every month. Jim would have to pay for some of this and the local authority would pay the rest.
> - Trying to get a more equal balance of support throughout Jim's family. The son continues to help in the late evening in putting Jim to bed but he has not extended his involvement. Maureen looks exhausted and the home care worker has told Sharma how snappy and bad-tempered she has been with Jim on occasion. The younger daughter, Jane, only calls round for a couple of hours at the weekend.
> - Trying the option of residential care.
>
> Some form of review needs to take place. The care plan needs to be re-negotiated. If Jim continues to stay in the community, it is now likely that the cost of supporting him there will be greater than the cost of a place in a residential home.

Assessing need

The example of Jim Lafferty aims to illustrate the process of care management and the tasks involved. It is clear that assessment is a crucial part of the seven tasks of care management and the rest of the chapter will cover further aspects of it.

User-led assessment of need

One of the key ideas within the community care changes was the emphasis that such assessments should be 'needs-led' or 'user-led'. Prior to the 1990/93 changes many assessors had been very conscious of what services were available and assessments had been tailored to these. In this sense they were 'service-led'. The intention of the changes was that appropriate services should be provided based on a full assessment of need.

One of the main objectives of the NHS&CC Act 1990 was to move towards more user-led assessments. The White Paper stressed that:

- 'The objective of assessment is to determine the best available way to help the individual.
- Assessments should focus positively on what the individual can and cannot do, and could be expected to achieve, taking account of his or her personal and social relationships.
- Assessment should not focus only on the user's suitability for a particular existing service.'

(DoH, 1989b, p. 18)

What should be assessed and how?

There are different aspects of need and the guidance divides this into six broad areas. A full comprehensive assessment of need should cover all these areas:

- personal/social care;
- health care;
- accommodation;
- finance;
- education/employment/leisure;
- transport/access.

(DoH, 1991a, p. 12)

Many local authorities have quite long assessment forms to be filled in. Assessors need to think about the **needs** of each individual case as every situation is different. It is generally good practice to try initially to build up a relationship and to explore informally why help is being sought at this stage. It is better not to be rushed into the stage of filling in a long complicated assessment form. However, social services agencies are under pressure and the ideal approach is often not possible because of a shortage of resources.

Unmet need

In the first few months of the community care changes there was a lot of concern about unmet need. This is where a need may be identified through an assessment but the authority is unable to meet it through lack of resources. Social Services Departments deal with this in three different ways:

- some are open about it with users and acknowledge it;
- some gather together the information in a collective way but avoid feeding it back to individual users;
- some neither record it in relation to individuals nor collectively.

In the early months of the implementation of the community care changes, local authorities were worried that if they recorded unmet need and made that knowledge available, they would be open to challenge through the courts using the judicial review process. Judicial review is the key legal mechanism by which the decisions of public bodies or officers can be challenged and overturned. Actions start in the High Court and may also go to the Court of Appeal and the House of Lords. It was felt that there would be a lot of scope for judicial reviews over the issue of unmet need. During 1993 only one situation came to court.

This was the situation of Mark Hazell which is discussed in Chapter 8.

Challenging assessments

There are several ways in which assessments can be challenged:

1 The user can use the complaints procedure. Under the 1990 NHS&CC Act each department has to have a complaints procedure.
2 The user can complain to the Secretary of State on the grounds that the Local Authority is in default of its duty under the Act.
3 The user can complain to the Local Government Ombudsman.
4 The user can contact their local councillor or Member of Parliament.
5 The user can take legal action through the courts with the use of the judicial review procedure.

Fast track assessment for drug and alcohol misusers

Drug and alcohol misusers compete for money with other users such as frail elderly people and disabled people. It all comes out of the same local authority community care budget. After the transfer of money from Social Security to Social Services in April, 1993, there was considerable concern that these users would receive a worse service and that resources for them would decline.

One reason for this is that many people with drug and alcohol problems move about frequently and may not have a settled residence. One fear was that Social Services Departments would be hesitant to pay for several weeks' or several months' expensive residential rehabilitation when the person was not an obviously settled resident in their area.

Local authorities are responsible for assessing the needs of alcohol and drug misusers and for arranging appropriate packages of care. The government recommended that fast track assessment procedures should be in place for these groups.

Fast track assessment is the rapid assessment of individual need of those people whose circumstances indicate that the timescales for the normal assessment process would result in:

- serious deterioration in their physical, social and emotional functioning and well-being;
- loss of motivation to accept care and treatment.

There are special circumstances for those with alcohol and drug problems. These circumstances may give rise to particular needs which for some will indicate the need for access to a fast track assessment process. Particular attention should be given to the fact that many alcohol and drug users may:

- present a range of complex problems;
- not have had previous contact with local authority Social Services Departments;
- be fearful about approaching statutory agencies for help;
- be seeking help in an authority other than their area of ordinary residence;
- have poor or changeable motivation;
- move about a lot;
- have accommodation difficulties or be homeless;

- not have strong social networks;
- have serious family and relationship problems;
- be particularly vulnerable to hepatitis and HIV/AIDS and their general health care is likely to be poor;
- have no financial resources and may not be in receipt of benefits;
- have been involved in, or the subject of, criminal activity.

(LGDF, 1993, p.4)

Multi-disciplinary assessment

Multi-disciplinary assessment is usually essential for a comprehensive assessment. There is a clear expectation that there will be far more multi-disciplinary assessments undertaken than in the past. This was stressed in the White Paper, *Caring For People*, which stated that: 'all agencies and professions involved with the individual and his or her problems should be brought into the assessment procedure when necessary' (DoH, 1989b, p. 19).

This statement is followed by a list of about twenty different kinds of workers who might be involved, indicating that multi-disciplinary working is easier to proclaim as an intention than to actually put into operation.

Often assessments are needed because of a crisis of some kind. The crisis may bring on pressure to enter residential care. This might be because there is no acceptable place to go after a period in hospital. By the nature of events this will often mean that the assessment has to be done quickly. Multi-disciplinary assessments take a lot of time and there is a tension here between the need for action and the need for time to make a thorough assessment.

Separation of assessment and service provision

A central thrust of government policy has been towards creating a split between purchaser and provider (see p. 6). This idea has influenced the model of care management that has been put forward by the Department of Health.

The Practitioners' Guide says that the stage of assessment will require a significant change of attitude from the practitioner, particularly in making 'conscious efforts to treat the assessment of need as a separate exercise from consideration of service response' (DoH, 1991a, p. 47).

The recommended position seems to be one of the care manager dealing with the seven stages but entirely on the purchaser side of the purchaser/provider split. The care manager will choose between provision from in-house services (which will be costed) and from services in the independent and private sectors. In this way some kind of market situation is brought into social services provision. We have here two ideas which the government is promoting — care management and purchaser/provider. The government's advice is that care management will be on the purchaser side but over time it may be that different models may emerge.

An improved service for blind and partially sighted people?

One writer argues that the community care changes present Social Services Departments with an opportunity to dramatically raise the levels of assessment and service provision to blind and partially sighted people. Williams argues that this will happen if care management procedures are adopted. She writes,

> Good social work and care management practice, demanding ongoing assessment, shared and agreed plans, monitoring and reviews, is not the norm in this area of work, which is dogged by a shortage of qualified staff, by large numbers of referrals and by its low priority status in most authorities.
>
> (Williams, 1993, p. 89)

Activity

It would be worthwhile trying to find out how the issues covered in this chapter are progressing at the local level in your area. If you are working within a Social Services Department, or know someone who is, you could find out how they are organizing care management and assessment.

Key questions

1 What are the seven tasks within the Department of Health's version of care management?
2 What are the main factors which have led to our current understanding of care management?
3 List the broad areas which should be covered in a comprehensive assessment.
4 What is a care plan?
5 In what ways might an assessment be challenged?
6 What is a Fast Track Assessment and who might it be used for?

Further reading

DoH(1991a), *Care Management and Assessment: Practitioners' Guide*, HMSO, London, 1991.

DoH,(1991b), *Care Management and Assessment: Managers' Guide*, HMSO, London, 1991. These two useful and important publications give Government guidance on care management and assessment.

The Disability Alliance, *Disability Rights Handbook*.

The Child Poverty Action Group, *National Welfare Benefits Handbook* and *Rights Guide to Non-means Tested Benefits*.
These two annual publications are valuable guides for health and social care workers, providing details and advice on the full welfare benefits available to users of community care services.

6

Abuse and harm

Preview

This chapter considers two key issues concerned with community care:

○ the abuse of adults by carers;
○ adult service users who harm themselves or others.

The protection of adult users from abuse

Chapter 5 covered how the 1990 NHS&CC Act requires Social Services Departments to carry out assessments of need. In considering assessment it is important to mention the issue of abuse. Some adults are at risk of abuse from people who care for them, though to a large extent adult abuse has been a hidden issue. Nationally, attention has been focused most on abuse of children. In relation to adults the abuse of elders has received some attention but abuse can involve any vulnerable adult. Policies, procedures and practice need to be developed in relation to all groups.

Carers of all types – paid or unpaid and in various circumstances – are capable of abuse. It might occur in:

- a person's own home;
- a carer's home;
- a residential home;
- a nursing home;
- a day care setting;
- a hospital.

Most carers, paid and unpaid, put in a tremendous amount of time, effort, love and concern so in some ways it may be hard for them to acknowledge that sometimes real abuse takes place. However the protection of adults at risk of abuse needs to be a central issue of concern in considering community care. There is a need to know more about it and how to respond to it. The following true case study gives an example of abuse by carers:

John Worton

C*ase study*   John Worton died in 1987. He was a retired labourer who had a stroke and lived in a local authority home in Birmingham. He went to live with one of his daughters and their family, against the advice of the home's staff and his other daughter. His living accommodation was very poor. However between June and December he had contact at different times with a district nurse, a GP, a nursing auxiliary, a social work assistant, day centre staff and his other daughter. He died on 25 December, 1987. When the police investigated, they discovered that he had been locked in his room. The post-mortem found that he was covered in bruises, had two broken ribs which were ten days old and that he had not eaten for three days. The coroners' jury gave a verdict of 'unlawful killing'. The case was referred to the Crown Prosecution Service but they did not prosecute.

(Channel 4, Dispatches, 1993)

A key aspect of oppression has been seen as a lack of power. This can be a lack of power in society or a lack of power in the community. There can also be a lack of power within a relationship and a symptom of this can be the abuse of the cared-for person.

Health and social care workers need to be concerned about the needs of those being cared for and those doing the caring. Only some Social Services Departments have guidelines or procedures for the protection of vulnerable adults. There is not sufficient acknowledgement of the potential for abuse. However, health and social care workers have to be open to the possibility that abuse may be happening.

> In 1992 Cathy O'Neill was killed in the London Borough of Hammersmith and Fulham. She was a 66-year-old disabled woman. She needed a replacement carer at short notice and she contacted a private domiciliary care agency. Cathy was murdered by her paid carer.
> At present, there are no statutory measures to register and inspect domiciliary care agencies. There is no requirement to do police checks on carers.

While there is coverage of assessment of need within the NHS&CC Act 1990, there is no coverage of what to do if someone is being abused and no coverage of the investigation of abuse. However in 1993 the government published national practice guidelines on dealing with abuse of elderly people in their own homes. These were called, *No Longer Afraid: Practice Guidelines* (DoH, 1993c) and were written by the Social Services Inspectorate (SSI). In these SSI guidelines it was stressed how they were compatible with the principles of sound assessment and care management and that they should be incorporated within these procedures:

Agencies should consider how they will ensure that this area of work is effectively handled within the context of their procedures for care management and assessment.

(DoH, 1993c, p.9)

The media treatment — an example of ageism?

Contrast the media treatment of the Cleveland child sexual abuse situation with the report on abuse of elderly people at Nye Bevan Lodge in Southwark. The initial reporting of both was at about the same time during the summer of 1987. The first led to a major press campaign, a government inquiry and changes to the law and procedures. The second had two or three paragraphs in the papers and disappeared from the news very quickly.

One commentator wrote about the inquiry into the Nye Bevan Lodge in Southwark: 'It is self-evident that when elderly, often confused residents are made to eat their own faeces, left unattended, physically manhandled, forced to pay money to care staff and even helped to die, something is seriously wrong.'

(Vousden, 1987, p. 19)

What do we mean by abuse?

There is no standard definition of abuse but there are recognized types:

* physical;
* emotional;
* financial;
* sexual;
* neglect;
* institutional.

Extent of abuse

The extent of abuse is linked to the issue of what is defined as abuse and is an equally difficult area. For example, do we include financial and emotional abuse and what sort of behaviour do we include within each category? Abuse is also bound to be 'hidden' to a large extent in that it is not something which people will readily admit to and talk about.

In 1992 the Channel 4 programme, *Dispatches,* commissioned the Office of Population, Census and Surveys to survey elder abuse. This survey involved a sample of 2130 people at 100 sites and 593 of these were over 60. Ten per cent of the whole sample admitted abusing elderly people and five per cent of elderly people reported abuse. This study excluded older people suffering from dementia. The SSI guidelines say that:

> . . . the scale of the problem is not known nor whether it is on the increase. There is no accepted way of recording reported cases, let alone unreported or undetected cases.
>
> (DoH, 1993c, p. 3)

Sexual abuse of adults with learning difficulties

A publication called *It could never happen here!* (ARC and NAPSAC, 1993) draws on some recent research to suggest that there are probably 800 new cases of sexual abuse of adults with learning disabilities in Britain every year. It argues that in general, services for this user group are not well-equipped to begin to deal with this issue. A first step is to ensure that everyone is prepared to admit that 'it can happen here' and that 'it probably will happen here – especially if we don't do anything to stop it.'

Causes of abuse

The SSI guidelines acknowledge that there are likely to be many different reasons for the abuse of older people:

> Carers under stress, or ill-equipped for the caring role, and carers who have been (and are still being) abused themselves, account for a proportion of cases. A history of poor family relationships is a reason for others. In some families the power once exercised by the parent is also probably a factor. Research, mainly from Canada and the USA, is beginning to reveal the complex nature of the problem.
>
> (DoH, 1993c, p. 4)

Equal opportunities and abuse

The guidelines state that:

> Any policy statement should reflect equal opportunities principles and ensure issues concerning race, gender, sexuality, age and disability are addressed.
>
> (DoH, 1993c, p. 9)

What to do when you suspect abuse?

If you are a paid or unpaid worker with an adult who you suspect has been abused, you should not ignore it. Some Social Services Departments have guidelines on what to do and you should follow those guidelines. Usually this would involve discussing your suspicions with your line manager in the first instance.

The publication on sexual abuse of adults with learning difficulties in residential settings (ARC and NAPSAC, 1993, p. 111) has a useful list of Do's and Don'ts when someone tells you they have been sexually abused. This is reproduced in the boxes below:

DO
- believe the person;
- stay calm;
- listen patiently;
- reassure the person they are doing the right thing in telling you;
- explain what you are going to do:
  if necessary, you will get emergency medical treatment;
  you will treat the information seriously;

you will report to the appropriate manager;
you and the manager will take steps to protect the individual;
- report to the appropriate manager as soon as you can;
- follow your own service guidelines concerning police involvement. In most circumstances, it is likely that a decision to call the police would rest with a manager, not a direct care worker. However, in an emergency and when a manager cannot be contacted, you should inform the police if you suspect that a crime (eg. a sexual assault or rape) has taken place;
- write a factual account of the conversation you had with the individual as soon as you can. Try as far as possible to write down the person's own words. This report should be given to your manager. It may later be used as part of a legal action.

DON'T
- appear shocked, horrified, disgusted or angry;
- press the individual for details (it is not your job to launch into an investiga- tion);
- make comments or judgements, other than to show sympathy and concern;
- contaminate or remove possible forensic evidence. If the reported incident has happened very recently it may still be possible for the police to obtain forensic evidence. Do not give the person a wash, a bath, or food or drink until after the medical examination;
- promise to keep secrets – you have a duty to pass on the information to the appropriate person;
- give sweeping reassurances such as, 'Now you have told someone this will never happen to you again' – no-one can give such a guarantee;
- confront the alleged abuser.

Carers, whether paid or unpaid, can reach a level of stress where they feel like verbally abusing or physically abusing the person they are caring for. The crucial point is to recognize this and to prevent it happening. In the short term, at a point of crisis, the carer should make the person safe and get out of the room. Pent-up anger and tension can then be expressed by punching a cushion, screaming into a pillow, going for a walk or whatever else works. In the longer term extra help and assistance will need to be pressed for to prevent the stress and tension resulting in harm to the person being cared for.

Change in the law?

Many feel that the national practice guidelines on the abuse of older people produced in 1993 are not enough and that there is a need for a change in the law. Currently the legal framework does not exist for workers to intervene unless a person is 'mentally disordered'. Without the law on their side profes- sional workers are limited in what they can do. The carer can refuse to let professionals have access. The adult victim may refuse help.

In 1993 a Law Commission report was produced which sets out for the first time what some statutory powers might look like. The report noted that there were some existing powers under Section 47 of the National Assistance Act

1948 and under the Mental Health Act 1983. However the report said that, 'these powers are rarely invoked, may be difficult to exercise and still leave some people unprotected'(Law Commission, 1993, p. 9.)

There is a growing appreciation of the need for powers for local authorities to protect incapacitated and vulnerable adults from abuse. Though there is some protection for residents in residential care homes and nursing homes through the Registered Homes Act 1984 and its associated regulations, there is a growing feeling that powers to investigate should also apply in these situations.

Abuse in nursing homes

The nurses' regulatory body, the United Kingdom Central Council for Nursing, Midwifery and Health Visiting issued a report in 1994 which showed that complaints about staff of nursing homes had more than doubled in three years. The council called for more inspectors to be recruited to check on the fast-growing nursing-home sector. The number of private nursing homes has risen from about 1,350 in 1986 to about 5,000 in 1994.

One example in the report was of a 58-year-old woman nurse who required six mentally-confused residents to be woken as early as 5.30 am to be washed and dressed. Another example was a male nurse who assaulted residents and slept while on duty. Both were struck off the nurses' register.

The report's proposals for matrons and managers included:

* a charter of residents' rights to be instated;
* procedures for recording all accidents and untoward incidents to be improved;
* a formal complaints procedure to be in place and understood by all staff;
* adequate staffing to be provided for good continuity of care.

(UKCC,1994)

Service users who harm themselves or others

This chapter has concentrated on abuse towards adults who are frail and vulnerable and who are often service users. More familiar because of media coverage is the situation of service users who either abuse themselves or abuse their carers or others in the community. For example, Ben Silcock, a schizophrenic, was severely mauled when he climbed into the lions' enclosure at London Zoo in December, 1992. This and other incidents led to a review in 1993 by the Department of Health of procedures for the care of mentally distressed people in the community.

The 1983 Mental Health Act covers this group of users in a general sense. It lays out:

* the procedures for the compulsory admission of people to hospital;
* the position and rights of people in hospital;
* the circumstances of their treatment;
* the procedures for their continued detention;
* the procedures for their discharge.

The 1993 DoH review was particularly concerned with seriously mentally distressed people living in the community. Two specific outcomes of the review, announced in the summer of 1993, were that:

- Legislation is to be brought in to allow for a new power called Supervised Discharge. The proposal includes tightening up the arrangements for discharge for a small group of people thought to be a danger to themselves or others. A key worker will be appointed for each person with clear responsibilities and accountability for ensuring that the agreed services and treatments are provided. Key workers allocated to the 3,000 or so former hospital patients will normally be community psychiatric nurses. Health authorities in this instance will have the lead responsibility.
- From October, 1994, hospitals and community health units have had to set up registers of seriously mentally ill people who are discharged to live in their own homes. The registers are to include the details of about 3,000 people considered to be at risk of relapsing into a condition where they would be a threat to themselves or others.

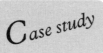

Christopher Clunis

Christopher Clunis was born in London in 1963. His parents came from Jamaica. In December, 1992, Christopher Clunis stabbed and killed Jonathan Zito on the platform of a tube station. An inquiry, chaired by Jean Ritchie, QC, was set up into the care of Clunis prior to this event and to make recommendations into the future delivery of care for people in similar circumstances (Ritchie, 1994).

The Ritchie Report gives the view that Clunis' care was 'a catalogue of failure and missed opportunity' (p. 105). The report describes in some detail the way in which there were failings in care from 1987 until 1992. Over this period at least ten hospitals and two Social Services Departments gave him care and treatment. Clunis was remanded to prison twice and stayed in several different hostels, resettlement units and bed and breakfast hotels. He also had contact with GPs, the police, housing officials and primary health care teams. Agencies were extremely poor at passing on information or trying to find it. 'He received care and treatment that was not effective in keeping him well or the public safe' (p. 105).

The Ritchie Report makes this statement about whether Christopher Clunis (a black person) had encountered racism:

> We record that no example of such prejudice or discrimination has been apparent to us, save for the possibility of too great a willingness to accept that he had abused drugs. (p 4.)

Vernon Harris, in a paper for the Race Equality Unit, argues that the Ritchie Report lacks a black perspective. The inquiry team did not include black or ethnic minority people amongst its membership. Harris puts the view that while the Inquiry team may not have found overt acts of racism in the treatment of Christopher Clunis, they neglected institutional racism (see p. 46). He argues that the treatment given to black people by the mental health service is both qualitatively and quantitatively different from that offered to white people. He writes,

> The Christopher Clunis case is undoubtedly a tragedy, but a double tragedy that those tasked with a review of his case failed to discern the patterns permeating the extensive information which they had efficiently amassed. In so doing, they

relegated to obscurity the dominant factor in the case, namely that of Institutional Racism, thereby invalidating to a considerable extent their recommendations.

(Harris, 1994, p. 25)

It is of course important to keep matters in proportion. The vast majority of mentally distressed people, including those who have been diagnosed as schizophrenic, live safely in the community. However there are some people who are not receiving the care and treatment they need in order to protect themselves and others from harm. This number is estimated by the Ritchie Report to be about 3,000 – 4,000 nationwide. This group needs special care and treatment involving close supervision and support. The report argues that if the needs of this small group are not met then community care policies will be discredited.

The report fills 130 pages in some detail and there are 78 detailed recommendations. Implementation of these recommendations would help but the recurring theme of the report is of missed opportunities to do anything. For example:

- At one stage Clunis asked to see a psychiatrist in order to review the medication he was on but he was not seen for thirteen months.
- A GP who saw Clunis struck him off his list because he was abusive and threatening.
- Clunis stabbed a fellow hostel inmate and was charged with causing grievous bodily harm with intent. However the police made few efforts to trace the victim before the case came to court and no effort to obtain independent evidence. The case was dropped.
- During the fortnight before the murder of Jonathan Zito, Clunis was involved in a series of violent incidents which were not properly or effectively responded to.

At various points there was the opportunity to do something and the power to do something but it did not happen. Clunis repeatedly fell through the nets of care without overstretched agencies having the will and determination to stop it happening (Harrison, 1994, p. 21).

The problems with care in the community for people with severe mental health problems are considerable and they have received a lot of media attention. A report in 1994 by the Mental Health Foundation found again that services were confused, fragmented and under-resourced. At the time of writing it is clear that community care is not working for this group of users (Utting W, 1994).

*A*ctivity

Many authorities now have guidelines in relation to abuse of adults. It would be worth obtaining a copy from one of your local Social Services Departments and studying it. Consider its good points and any areas in which you feel it could be improved.

A ctivity

If you are doing caring work, consider if anyone who has been in your care has been subject to abuse. Consider what action was taken and what action might have been taken to prevent the abuse.

Key questions

- List some of the different types of abuse of adults.
- Do you think that there is a need for more legislation to protect vulnerable adults? Give reasons for your answer.
- Give two recommended outcomes of the 1993 Department of Health review of procedures for the care of the seriously mentally distressed in the community.

Further reading

Pritchard, J. 1992. *The Abuse of Elderly People: A Handbook For Professionals*, Jessica Kingsley, London, 1992. This is a useful handbook on elder abuse. The first half looks at the theory of abuse and how to recognize it. The second part gives exercises which can be adapted for different types of workers.

DoH(1993c), *No Longer Afraid*, HMSO, London, 1993. These are practice guidelines produced by the Department of Health to safeguard older people in domestic settings.

Ritchie, J., Dick, D. and Lingham, R. *The Report of the Inquiry into the Care and Treatment of Christopher Clunis*, HMSO, London, 1994. A thorough analysis of the care and treatment of Christopher Clunis.

Harris, V. *Review of the Report of the Inquiry into the Care and Treatment of Christopher Clunis: A Black Perspective*, Race Equality Unit, London, 1994.

Utting, W. et al. *Creating Community Care*, Mental Health Foundation, London, 1994. A report on community care for people with severe mental health problems.

7

Contracting and quality assurance

Preview

This chapter considers two key issues concerned with community care:

○ Purchaser/provider and contracting;
○ Quality assurance.

Purchaser/provider and contracting

Chapter 1 described how the internal market separating purchasers and providers had been created within both the NHS and Social Services Departments. Agreements between purchasers and providers are arrived at through contracts.

We saw in Chapter 1 how this development of markets within public services and the encouragement of contracting (both internally and with outside organizations) has formed part of the overall strategy of government policy since 1979. The intentions of this 'contract culture' are:

• to improve the quality of services;
• to obtain better value for money;
• to increase choice for the service user.

Objectives of purchaser/provider split

Figure 7.1 gives the objectives and assumed benefits of the purchaser/provider split. Government intention is that Social Services Departments will purchase more services from the private and voluntary sector.

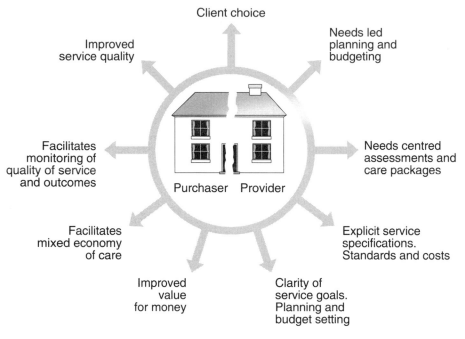

Client choice

Improved
service quality

Needs led
planning and
budgeting

Facilitates
monitoring of
quality of service
and outcomes

Needs centred
assessments and
care packages

Purchaser   Provider

Facilitates
mixed economy
of care

Explicit service
specifications.
Standards and costs

Improved
value
for money

Clarity of
service goals.
Planning and
budget setting

Figure 7.1: The expected benefits of separating purchasers/commissioners and providers (DoH, 1991c, p. 6).

Caring for people who live at home

The *Caring For People Who Live At Home* initiative was announced by the Department of Health in January, 1992. It had the aim of stimulating day services and domiciliary services within the private and voluntary sector. While there clearly is a variety of suppliers of residential care, this has not been the case in relation to day and domiciliary care.

Bids from local authorities were invited and 15 local authorities were selected. They have each been given funding to develop new practice and new thinking in this area. The initiative is managed and coordinated by a project team based at the Policy Studies Institute in London.

The intention of the community care changes was also that there should be some re-structuring within Social Services Departments. Each department would re-structure so that there was a clear purchaser section and a clear provider section. Thus the purchasers of services — the care managers or those supervising care managers – would be able to choose between services provided by their own department and those provided by outside agencies. Figure 7.2 gives an idea of this, with the care manager, who is aware of the needs of users, contracting for services with either in-house providers or private or voluntary service providers.

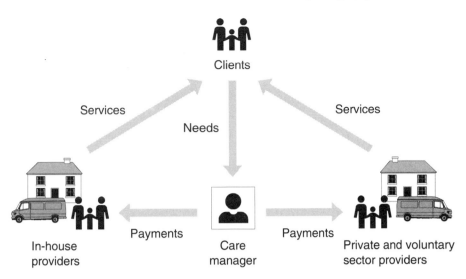

Figure 7.2: The care manager has the choice of contracting for services with either in-house providers or private or voluntary providers (DoH, 1991c, p. 10).

Contracting

It is not new for a range of organizations to provide services in social welfare. One way in which services have developed in the past has been by voluntary organizations identifying a need and then providing a small innovative service.

> Cases of women suffering physical abuse from their partners are examples of a need which was not being met by the statutory services. Starting in the 1960s, womens' refuges were set up by groups of women as a response to the need.

Sometimes initiatives by voluntary organizations have collapsed because of shortage of money. In other situations local authorities have responded by supporting the service with a grant or taking it over and expanding it. Where grants have been given, they usually depended on an agreement about how the money would be spent. Often, however, the details of what exactly would be provided were not specified – for example, how many people would receive the services.

Contracts make this arrangement tighter by introducing a legally enforceable arrangement in which the voluntary organization or private organization is given a specification for a job which has to be delivered in return for an agreed amount of money.

Specification means defining in written form the service that is to be delivered. Sometimes it is in general terms and sometimes it is detailed.

There are two main types of contract in use:

• block contracts, and;
• spot contracts.

Block contracts
These establish relationships between purchasers and providers which are expected to develop over time and cover a number of transactions. If there is a steady flow of demand then block contracts allow supply to be matched by demand.

Spot contracts
These are contracts which exist for the delivery of one particular service.

What goes into a contract

There are many different ways in which contracts can be drawn up. They may be short or long, simple or complicated. The areas which most contracts cover would include:

- the details of the service to be provided;
- the standards of the service;
- how performance of the contract will be monitored;
- the fees for the service and how these will be paid;
- what is to happen if either side fails to meet its obligations;
- the length of the agreement;
- the ways of settling any conflicts or disagreements.

The arrangements for community care mean that services will increasingly be put out to contract. At the present time there is not compulsory competitive tendering as there is in some parts of the public sector. Compulsory competitive tendering means that a local authority service must by law be put out to interested parties and organizations to bid for it. Currently in community care there is guidance and encouragement to move in the direction of contracting out services. The government has also specified that certain proportions of grant money given to local authorities must be channelled towards the voluntary and private sectors.

Equal opportunities and contracting

'Social Services Departments should seek to ensure that their contracting processes do not discriminate against women, people with disabilities, people from minority ethnic groups or their organizations. Within the limits permissable under Part 11 of the Local Government Act 1988, they should use relevant race relations and equal opportunities legislation to ensure that all services contracted out to non-statutory agencies are provided in an anti-racist and ethnically sensitive manner.'

(DoH, 1991d, p. 21)

Contracting: a contentious area

We saw in Chapter 1 that contracting is politically controversial. The government stresses greater choice, better quality and value for money through competition.

> The Government expects local authorities to promote and extend the use of indepen-
> dent providers in order to give more choice to the consumer and obtain the benefits of
> efficiency from increased competition.
>
> (DoH, 1991d, p. 6)

This expectation of expanding the use of independent providers has been encouraged in a number of ways. Since the 1990 NHS & CC Act, the Government has required:

* local authorities to consult over their community care plans with the independent sector;
* local authorities to include within their community care plans a statement saying how they intend to make arrangements to purchase residential and non-residential care from the independent sector;
* that a very high proportion of the transfer money to local authorities for community care should be spent in the independent sector.

Contracting may open up greater opportunities for user-involvement than in the past. For example, some opportunities to provide services may open up for black communities through the contracting system. Those who are awarded contracts could be local neighbourhood groups organized as 'community businesses'. In this way the 'enabling authority' could encourage and facilitate local, grass-roots community care.

There are, however, some disadvantages:

* The danger of contracts going to those organizations which make the cheapest bid. These might not be the best in terms of quality.
* There may be danger of corruption in the contracting process.
* Those awarded the contract might be large corporate businesses with little concern for the local area and neighbourhood.
* Community care in the informal sector is not concerned with commercial values. It is largely concerned with values of giving, obligation, love, and mutuality. In the past it has not involved a contract culture and it is possible that such a culture will undermine and cause considerable damage to these values.

The impact of contracting on the home care service

Before the community care changes, almost all domiciliary care was provided by Social Services home care sections. This is changing in various ways:

* More services are being run by voluntary organizations.
* There is a growth of services run by private firms. Some firms which have run residential homes in the past are diversifying into domiciliary care.
* Some care managers are negotiating individual help through contracts at a very local level. For example, they might arrange payment to a neighbour for performing certain tasks on a regular basis.

The purchaser/provider split and the development of the contract culture have happened in both the NHS and Social Services. This has opened up possibilities of District Health Authorities and Social Services Departments coming together and arranging contracts together. These ideas of 'joint commissioning' are at an early stage but, with similar structural changes within both health care and social care organizations, it seems likely that they will have an increasing appeal.

Quality Assurance

This section of the chapter emphasizes quality assurance within Social Services Departments because they are the lead authorities in relation to community care. However quality issues are also important in the health service, in the voluntary sector and in the private sector.

Caring For People noted that whenever Social Services Departments purchase or provide services they 'should take steps to ensure that the quality to be delivered is clearly specified and properly monitored, bearing in mind that vulnerable people are involved as users' (DoH, 1989b, p. 23).

The concerns with quality and the language associated with it are very much a part of the community care changes of the early 1990s. It is helpful first to clarify the meanings of some terms used.

Quality

'Quality' conveys a standard, so a concern with good quality means concern with good standards. Concern with quality also means a concern that the service is appropriate for the needs.

Quality Assurance

Quality Assurance is a cyclical process designed to ensure that the organization will provide quality services. It means:

- having procedures in place which ensure that the users have their needs met with a high quality service;
- setting standards for the service;
- building in a continuous monitoring of whether those standards are being met.

Total Quality Management

This is an approach to quality assurance which emphasizes the importance of changing attitudes at all levels in the organization. It is popular within the NHS and its goal is to establish a culture of quality, where quality is top of everyone's agenda. There is an involvement of all staff in clear and explicit quality objectives.

Quality control

Quality control involves having procedures to check on any difficulties and problems and then put them right. Whilst quality assurance is concerned with preventing any problems, quality control is concerned with having an effective system of finding out what the problems are and correcting them.

Is there a need for a community care charter?

The House of Commons Health Committee in its sixth report (HMSO, 1993) called for a charter for community care standards as a way of improving and maintaining quality:

> If the care in the community policy is to be implemented with users' and carers' interests at its heart, this suggests the need for a basic minimum of service which users and carers can expect and are entitled to. The Patient's Charter gives at least some basic standards against which health service users can judge the service they receive, including community care services provided by the NHS. Users of social care services have no equivalent . . .
>
> We recommend that the Government develop a Community Care Charter, as part of its Citizen's Charter initiative, drawing primarily on the views of user and carers, to provide some indication of the level and quality of service which citizens are entitled to expect as a result of its policy. We consider the issues which should be addressed in this Charter in this Report.
>
> (House of Commons, 1993, p. vii)

During the summer of 1994 the Department of Health issued a consultation document on guidelines for the production of local community care charters. Some argued that there should be national standards and entitlements but the likely outcome of the consultation period is that locally-based community care charters will be produced.

Chapter 1 described how two initiatives concerned with quality were part of the community care legislative changes. By April, 1991, each Social Services Department had to set up:

* a complaints procedure;
* an inspection unit.

In terms of the community care legislation it was these two elements concerned with quality which the government wanted in place at an early stage. We will look at each in turn.

A complaints system

Each Social Services Department was required to set up a complaints procedure by April, 1991. The guidance for setting up such a procedure says that there should be a 'designated complaints officer' so there should be someone clearly identifiable who is responsible for dealing with a complaint.
There should be three stages in the procedure:

Stage 1 – an informal or problem-solving stage;
Stage 2 – a formal or registration stage;
Stage 3 – a review stage.

Stage 1
The informal stage 1 is intended to ensure that users with a complaint can express their views and are listened to. If possible the complaint should be satisfactorily resolved at this stage. It is important to establish what changes the complainant wants to achieve.

Stage 2

It is hoped that many complaints will be sorted out at the informal first stage but if it is not, it goes to stage 2. At stage 2 the formal complaint needs to be put in writing, an investigator may need to be appointed, and it is recommended that the line manager is given an opportunity to take action on the written complaint before top management become involved.

Stage 3

If the complaint has not been settled at stage 2 then it goes to the Review Panel or stage 3 within 28 days of the complainant requesting a review. This panel is made up of three people. At least one of these should be an independent person and that person will chair the panel. The authority then has 28 days in which to decide whether to accept the view of the panel and on the action to be taken.

Arguments for and against complaints procedures

Arguments in favour

a   A complaints procedure can be seen as a way of giving some degree of power to users of services. A complaints procedure can make a contribution to 'empowering' users.

b   For a service trying to improve itself, complaints are one of the ways in which it receives feedback. By responding carefully and thoughtfully to the complaints that come in, a department can improve its overall performance. Thus a complaints procedure can be an important element of quality assurance.

c   Often people feel upset by the 'way' they are treated and so a complaints procedure should help to ensure that good standards of courtesy and respect are maintained.

Arguments against

a   Workers may see a complaints procedure as a 'threat'. None of us like our work to be the subject of a complaint. It could have an unsettling and demoralizing effect.

b   It can be seen to be unfair because the complaint may be registered against individual people but those people often have very little control over the resources and the quality of what is provided.

c   It may be felt that a complaints system is ineffective, a sop, rather than a mechanism for real change.

In many agencies there is some resistance to seeing complaints procedures in a positive light. Some people may take the view, 'Well, yes we have one because we have to have one but we do not publicize it because we have enough to do.'

Another aspect of this complaints procedure is that it is internal to the Department. It is only at the very last stage that any independent person is involved. As a procedure, it can clearly be criticized on this basis.

Equal opportunities issues and complaints procedures

There is the issue of whether a woman, a disabled person, a black person would feel that their situation was being sensitively and fairly considered through all the stages of a complaints procedure. For example, a physically disabled person might well want a physically disabled person to be part of the process of looking into their complaint. If their complaint reached stage 3, careful consideration should be given to the composition of the panel. The independent person (and the general composition of the panel) within stage 3 should be selected with equal opportunities issues being a major consideration.

Particular care also needs to be given to ensuring that vulnerable groups, such as those with learning or communication difficulties, can use the procedures and make complaints. Appropriate help needs to be available to enable this to happen.

Complaints within the NHS

The complaints procedures within the NHS have been complicated and cumbersome. The Government set up a committee to review NHS complaints procedures and this committee reported in 1994. The report argued for a unified complaints procedure and stressed that most complaints should be handled informally whenever possible. A much quicker system should be established. The publication of the report was followed by a period of consultation prior to changes being introduced.

The Patients' Charter sets out standards which should be met within the health service and also says that one's right is to have any complaint about NHS Services investigated and receive a full reply as soon as possible.

Inspection units

Prior to April, 1991, arrangements existed under the Registered Homes Act, 1984, to safeguard people in independent residential care and nursing homes. The White Paper, *Caring For People*, proposed inspection units for residential homes which are both independent and within the local authority. Because of this status of being within the local authority but with a degree of independence they have sometimes been called 'arms-length' inspection units. These units are structurally separate from the service management and provision arms of their Social Services Departments. They apply the same quality assurance criteria to all homes.

Aims of inspection units
The aims of the inspection units are:

- to ensure a good quality of life for people in public, private and voluntary residential care homes;
- to monitor the performance of managers;
- to advise local authorities on quality and cost effectiveness.

Organization of inspection units
How inspection units are organized is decided on a local basis but the inspection unit is overseen by an advisory committee which gives a voice to the independent sector and to users. Directors of Social Services have to report back each year on its operation to the Social Services Committee.

Arguments against inspection units being within Social Services Departments

- Inspection units have been described as 'arm's length' units. Each unit reports to the Director — the same Director who is responsible for the running of the local authority homes. With limited resources the Director may feel that she or he cannot do very much about any problems uncovered.
- Workers in the units may find it very hard to criticize the work of colleagues in the same authority.
- Unit workers could feel informal pressures not to criticize the workings of the same authority which pays their salaries.

Arguments for inspection units being within Social Services Departments

- It is cheaper and easier to make inspection units part of the Social Services Department.
- Independent units can be seen as too removed from the service to adequately realize what the pressures are and what is going on.
- Constructive dialogue to improve the quality of services may be more likely between colleagues within the same authority. Workers in residential homes may be less defensive when receiving criticism and see it as more legitimate.

Registration of private nursing homes and hospitals

The 1984 Registered Homes Act placed the responsibility for the registration of those wishing to provide private nursing home care or private hospital care on the Secretary of State for Health, who delegated that responsibility to health authorities. The 1990 NHS&CC Act did not change this arrangement in any way.

A report from the Royal College of Nursing in 1994 showed that people in private nursing homes were being placed at risk because inspectors were too overstretched to guarantee standards. Their survey of health authorities in England and Wales showed a wide variation in the quality of inspections.

By law, checks should be carried out at least twice a year. All authorities met their basic duty but staffing for doing this varied considerably. In one health authority only one full-time and two part-time inspectors were examining 267 homes with 4,110 beds. This contrasted with another authority where one full-time and one part-time inspector were covering seven premises with 269 beds.

In checking the fitness of prospective home managers, only 77% of authorities undertook a police check and only 17% requested a detailed curriculum vitae.

The Report argues that the 1984 law is not firm enough – it ignores the quality of care provided and allows authorities to make widely differing interpretations of their responsibilites.

(RCN, 1994)

Quality and standards

The 1990 NHS&CC Act gave a major impetus towards concern with quality. However inspection units and complaints procedures are concerned with services which have gone wrong in some way. They are a part of quality control (procedures to check on difficulties and problems) which is just a part of a concern about quality. The obvious but central aspect about quality is that it is the responsibility of everyone in the organization. Everyone has to be concerned with achieving good standards.

Quality is about standards and these define in detail what the service user can expect. Earlier in the chapter mention was made of specifications in relation to contracts. These specifications will usually include statements about standards. They need to be set out in such a way that it is relatively easy to judge whether or not they are being achieved.

Important indicators of quality for users

The House of Commons Health Committee in its sixth report (HMSO, 1993) drew on some comments from users who had spoken to them to make the following comment:

'Some of the quality indicators suggested by representatives of users among our witnesses were as follows:

"When service users. . . stopped reporting the attitude amongst workers that the worker knows more about the person's need than the person herself or himself".

"People do not keep saying they have been passed around from pillar to post and back again with no-one willing to take responsibility for their problem."

"When there is no person with a disability unwilling to be yet forced to be in a residential home, I think community care will be getting somewhere."

"When the 85-year-old mother and the 55-year old daughter she is looking after do not go to bed at night not knowing what is going to happen if the mother dies at night and they do not go to bed not knowing what will happen if the mother becomes ill." '

(House of Commons, 1993, p. v)

Social Services Departments that buy services need to:

- set their own standards of performance;
- monitor in what way services are not up to these standards;
- ensure it has mechanisms and sanctions to deal with shortfall.

A report on Quality Assurance by the Social Services Inspectorate writes,

Our experience in visiting local authorities is that we still have some way to go before even key standards of performance can be identified with any confidence. . .

(DoH, 1992b, p. 17)

The Social Services Inspectorate has produced a number of documents on standards under the general heading of *Caring For Quality*. One of these, for example, is *Guidance on Standards for Residential Homes for Elderly People* (DoH, 1990b).

British Standard 5750

This has been the national standard for all quality management systems and has therefore been applicable to the health care and social care systems. As from 1994 BS5750 became known as BS EN ISO 9000. Health and social care organisations apply to a certification body (such as the British Standards Institution) for assessment. BS5750 (now BS EN ISO 9000) sets down guidelines and principles that need to be addressed in the various activities of the organisation. These guidelines help an organisation create a cost-effective, quality conscious working environment. A number of services for health and social care have registered for it. It has the following advantages:

- It gives a clear statement and message that the organisation has systems and procedures aimed at producing a quality service.
- These have been thoroughly audited by an independent organisation.
- An organisation having certification is likely to have greater credibility in winning contracts.

N/SVQs and quality

Many people working in social and health care fields have not had a formal training but have considerable experience and expertise. N/SVQs are a way of recognizing expertise and skill. A few years ago in the local authority residential sector there was a lack of qualifications. Typically there would be one person in a residential home with a qualification, with the rest of the staff receiving no recognition for the work they did. One result of introducing N/SVQs was to help staff demonstrate that the work done is skilled and to empower people who have felt undervalued.

The development of N/SVQs is affecting the contracting process in both the NHS and local authorities. Providers are arguing that as part of the quality which they offer, N/SVQs show that competencies and skills are to be demonstrated within the workforce and the workplace. The competence levels are practised within the workplace as part of the contract. Having a workforce in possession of N/SVQs or obtaining N/SVQs becomes one way of demonstrating quality.

Purchasers of services are also inquiring about whether organizations they may contract with have workers involved with N/SVQs. N/SVQs should help to tell purchasers whether an organization is competent. If care workers within an organization cannot demonstrate competence, this raises serious questions about the competence of the whole organization. The process of assessment for N/SVQs may show up problems within organizations and management structures. Harvey and Tisdall write,

> In reality N/SVQs will serve as an important vehicle by which to identify the absence of competence and thus emphasize organizational or managerial shortcomings.

> (Harvey and Tisdall, 1992, p. 25)

*A*ctivity

If you are working within a Social Services Department, or know someone who is, try to see a copy of a contract between a voluntary organization and the local authority. This will give you have a better idea of what they are.

*A*ctivity

The local Social Services complaints' procedure should be available on a leaflet and it would be useful to obtain a copy of it and study it.

*A*ctivity

Inspection units produce annual reports on their work and your local inspection unit may be able to let you have a copy. Read it through and you will obtain a better idea of the work of these units.

Key questions
- What are the objectives of the purchaser/provider split?
- What goes into a contract?
- What are some advantages and some disadvantages of contracting?
- What are some key elements of quality assurance?
- What are the different stages of a complaints procedure?
- What are the arguments for and against inspection units being within Social Services Departments?

Further reading

Leat, D. *The Development of Community Care by the Independent Sector*, PSI, London, 1993. This review describes the available research material on the development of the independent sector in community care. It is designed to be a practical guide to local authorities and to providers or would-be providers in the independent sector.

DoH(1991c), *Implementing Community Care; Purchaser, Commissioner and Provider Roles*, HMSO, London, 1991.

DoH(1991d), *Purchase of Service; Practice Guidance*, HMSO, London, 1991.

DoH(1991e), *The Right to Complain: Practice Guidance on Complaints Procedures in Social Services Departments*, HMSO, London, 1991.

8

User empowerment in community care

Preview

This chapter considers:

○ how user empowerment is described in various community care reports and in the community care legislation;.
○ the importance of information as a starting point for empowerment;
○ an example from Birmingham of involvement and empowerment;
○ two models of empowerment: 'consumerist' and 'participatory';
○ the main constraints surrounding user empowerment;
○ a way forward for empowerment.

Background to user empowerment

User empowerment involves shifting the balance of power so that users have more power and professional workers have less. Different words are used — sometimes 'empowerment', sometimes 'involvement', sometimes 'participation', sometimes 'consumerism'. This chapter explores this movement towards greater equality between the users and the providers of community care.

In 1985 the House of Commons Social Services Committee Report on Community Care wrote:

> We have had difficulty in hearing the authentic voice of the ultimate consumers of community care. There have been considerable advances in techniques designed to enable and encourage mentally ill or handicapped people to speak for themselves. . . . But there is a long way to go. Services are still mainly designed by providers and not users, whether families or clients, and in response to blueprints rather than in answer to demand. Matching the service to the consumer rather than vice versa should be the one central aim of community care in the future (Para 31).

We have seen in Chapter 1 how the Audit Commission Report and Griffiths Report were concerned primarily with structural and financial issues. However, Griffiths' promotion of the 'enabling authority' was intended to promote diversity and thus widen choice for users. This idea was embedded in the White Paper *Caring For People* (DoH, 1989b). One of the three fundamental aims of the White Paper was to 'give people a greater individual say in how they live their lives and the services they need to help them to do so'(p. 4).

Two ways in which the Government intended this to happen were:

- by each Social Services Department setting up a complaints procedure for users;
- by consultation with users in relation to community care plans.

Later practice guidance from the Department of Health gave further emphasis to involving users and increasing their choice. The guidance used the language of empowerment. For example, study this extract from the Practitioners' Guide to Care Management:

> The rationale for this reorganization is the empowerment of users and carers. Instead of users and carers being subordinate to the wishes of service providers, the roles will be progressively adjusted. In this way, users and carers will be enabled to exercise the same power as consumers of other services. This redressing of the balance of power is the best guarantee of a continuing improvement in the quality of service.
>
> (DoH, 1991a, p. 9)

The National Users and Carers Group

In 1993 a 'National Users and Carers Group' was set up by the Government. This was a group of over 20 service users and carers set up as a watchdog body to overlook community care and help shape its future. It has the job of tackling those local authorities or health authorities which were failing to involve users and carers. It was also given the job of reporting regularly its findings to senior civil servants and ministers.

In the practice guidance, *Purchase of Service*, there is also an emphasis on the rights of users and carers as consumers:

> The White Paper, *Caring For People*, and the NHS & CC Act puts clients' choice, consumer rights and the needs of carers at the forefront and presents SSDs and social services committees with a major opportunity to reshape or extend their policies, procedures and practice to achieve these objectives.
>
> (DoH, 1991d, p. 2)

Information is power

Information is a starting point for empowerment. This aspect is stressed within the government guidance. There are many areas in which health and social care organizations need to consider whether their users have been given information. Amongst these would be details of the complaints procedure, details of the community care plan, details of eligibility in relation to services, and details of their rights to see the records kept on them. The 1980s did see some changes in relation to access to user records. These were:

1 The Data Protection Act 1984 allows people to see information about themselves which is stored on computer. Service users whose records are kept on computer are entitled to see any information about themselves.

2 The Access to Health Records Act 1990 gives people access to paper records. Patients are allowed access to those records which were written after the Act

came into force in November, 1991. The law applies to records held by both hospitals and GPs. However it does allow a doctor or health authority to refuse access to any information which might – in the doctor's opinion – threaten the patient's mental or physical health if they were to see it.

3 The Access to Medical Reports Act 1988 gives access to medical reports relating to someone, supplied by a medical practitioner for insurance or employment purposes.

4 With the Access to Personal Files Act, 1987, users gained the right to make a written request for access to manually held personal information within housing and Social Services Departments. The Department must reply within 40 days.

Few people ask to see their files, but the sharing of what is being written can be built into everyday practice by health and social care workers. There should be no problem with a regular offer of, 'Do you want to see what I have written?' Alternatively, a worker can suggest, 'I have bought along a draft of what I have written to discuss.'

A woman involved in developing access to records policy in a social services department made the following comment about the link between access to records and changing power relationships:

'By sharing records you're equalizing the balance of power, changing the state of knowledge. It changes your practice when you get faced by the client'

(Beresford and Croft, 1993b, p. 170).

The community care changes raise the possibility of empowering users by providing them with full information. For example, users should have information about:

- complaints procedures;
- possibilities for someone to represent them or act as advocate for them;
- who is entitled to which services and the criteria for making decisions;
- the drawing up of service specifications in contracts and what role they or their representatives can have in the process;
- a copy of any care plan drawn up for the user;
- the monitoring process of the service provided and how the user may play a part in this;
- the agency's policy on confidentiality.

For this information to be accessible to all, there needs to be an effective translation and interpreter service. Consideration needs to be given as to how it can be made available to blind and partially sighted people (for example, in braille or on cassette tape).

An example of involving users — the Birmingham Community Care Special Action Project

Involving users takes time, effort and commitment as is illustrated with the example of the Community Care Special Action Project (CCSAP) started by Birmingham City Council in 1987. The two key principles guiding the project were:

- that responsibility for community care should rest not only with health authorities and the Social Services Department, but with the local authority as a whole;
- that people who use services should be consulted and should influence the way in which services were developed.

(Barnes, 1993, p. 127)

The initiative ranged very widely but a key element of it was a programme of consultation with carers, and we will focus on this. One theme of CCSAP was the recognition that community care policies are very dependent on the role of family members, friends and neighbours in providing care. The consultation programme was set up to try to ensure that services developed in a way that was responsive to the needs of carers and supportive of their role.

This consultation took place by a series of meetings throughout the city. The meetings were held in what the organizers hoped were appropriate local venues such as day centres, schools, and community centres. It was intended to be an opportunity for carers to share and express their problems about services to senior local authority officers. Chief officers and senior officers were involved in chairing them – part of the intention was to make sure that they heard about some of the problems which carers experienced. Three 'rounds' of consultations took place.

The first two rounds held in 1987/88 and 1988/89 comprised 12 meetings attended by about 350 people. Eleven action points came out of this. These were key areas for improving the quality and effectiveness of services provided by the council and the health authorities. The eleven action points were:

1 more information about services;
2 improving notification of unavoidable changes to services;
3 notifying the name and telephone number of people who visit carers at home so that they can be contacted again;
4 assistance with taking holidays;
5 improving opportunities for respite care which allows carers to take a break;
6 dealing with concerns about the future care of the people cared for;
7 improvements in special transport provided by the council and in public transport services generally;
8 the problem of social isolation;
9 the need for specialist equipment and adaptations;
10 the need for help outside normal office hours;
11 improvements in day care provision.

The third round of consultation took place in 1989/90, partly to feed back progress on the eleven key points. This round involved twelve meetings, one in each Parliamentary Constituency. Three hundred and five carers were consulted in this round.

A fourth round of consultation was specifically aimed at reaching black and ethnic minority carers. It took place in 1991. This particular consultation was given as an acknowledgment that these groups had been under-represented at the previous consultations.

Two 'carers panels' were set up and these met regularly at the council buildings. They have provided an on-going point of contact with the city council services and personnel. They are a way in which carers can directly monitor the action taken by the city and the health authorities.

Two models of empowerment

Two different ways (or models) of considering empowerment are particularly helpful. One model of empowerment is that of the consumer who has greater 'choice' of services. This is called the *consumerist* model. An alternative model is one where the user has greater control over the services and we call this the *participatory* model. In reality a project such as the Birmingham CCSAP would probably not fit neatly into either model, having elements of both. Nevertheless looking at it in this way does help to emphasize different perspectives on empowerment. We will look at each model in turn.

Consumerist model

This model views users as consumers. The parallel is with consumers in the economic market place or the retail market place. Essentially the user has a greater choice between the services on offer.

Consumerism in the public services means bringing some of the principles of the market place to bear. We have seen how changes towards creating more of a market place within health and social care provision are underway. Social services departments have to:

- move towards a mixed economy of care;
- become more of an enabling authority;
- encourage the private sector;
- make greater use of contracts;
- have a purchaser/provider split.

These changes represent a significant break from the past in most departments and it is this general approach which has underpinned the 1990 legislation.

Key elements of the 'consumerist' approach to public services are that the user has:

- more choice because of the greater range of services provided. The purchaser/provider split is seen as crucial in enabling this to happen.

- more and clearer information about the services available and clear information about who the services are for;
- the availability of representation or advocacy for users, although we have seen that this is only in the guidance rather than in the legislation itself;
- access to a complaints procedure.

A critique of the consumerist model

The consumerist model emphasizes information for users and user-involvement but is not really concerned with user-power. Customers in a shop can choose between the limited selection of products which are on display. They do have a certain choice between different products and between different shops. However they do not determine what is put on the shelf. They have very little power in relation to what they can choose from.

Consumerism in health and welfare services can be criticized in similar terms. Choice may be expanded to some extent. For example, there may be a choice between three day centres an older person can attend. This is a good thing but the choice is still limited. Further stages of choice would involve users in decisions such as whether they want day centres, where the day centres are, what goes on in them and how decisions are taken within them.

The consumerist model lacks this dimension of power over what is provided and how it is provided. Oppressed groups in society share a lack of power. Anti-oppressive work by health and social care workers is about empowering people and so we need to look at practice in relation to increasing power. This leads into another model of empowerment which is called participatory.

Participatory model

In this model there is a notion of users having a greater say and control over services. The model goes beyond greater choice to some control and say in the provision of services. This model draws on traditions of community work and community action. These traditions have always strongly emphasized power and participation issues.

Chapter 3 mentioned organizations that have campaigned for greater direct control and say over services. The British Deaf Association is an example of such an organization with a long history. Survivors Speak Out and People First are more recent examples.

The Survivors Speak Out conference in Edale in 1987 agreed a charter of needs and demands. Some of the listed items of the charter in the box below give a good sense of some of the key elements of the participatory model:

---

1 Mental health service providers recognize and use people's first-hand experience of emotional distress for the good of others.
2 Refuge is provided, planned and under the control of survivors of psychiatry.
3 Free counselling is available for all.
4 There is a choice of services, including self-help alternatives.

---

5   There is a government review of services, with recipients sharing their views.
6   There is provision of resources to implement self-advocacy for all users.
7   Adequate funding is available for non-medical community services, especially crisis intervention.
8   Users and ex-users of services are represented on statutory bodies, including Community Health Councils, Mental Health Review tribunals and the Mental Health Act Commission.
9   Full access to all personal medical records is available to users.
10   Legal protection and means of redress is available for all psychiatric patients.
11   The democratic right of staff to refuse to administer any treatment, without risk of sanction or prejudice is established.
12   Electro-convulsive therapy and psycho-surgery are phased out.
13   Drug use and its consequences are independently monitored.
14   All patients are provided with full written and verbal information on treatments, including adverse findings.
15   There is an end to discrimination against people who receive, or have received, psychiatric service with particular regard to housing, employment, insurance etc.

(Survivors Speak Out, 1988, p. 26)

Getting involved can transform peoples' lives, affirm what they feel and give them confidence. This can happen in a variety of ways. For example:

- People can gain confidence from the process of being involved.
- They can obtain support and help from other users in similar situations and circumstances.
- They can begin to see that they can have some control over aspects of their lives.
- They can begin to feel and acknowledge their own skills and abilities.

Here is one example:

'I went to this meeting on disability. I heard a lot of people saying things that I had thought myself but never said. I'd never put them into words myself. I was terrified when I first got involved. I never thought I'd be able to do things like speak publicly and have the confidence to do things that other people were doing. But I've built up the skills and confidence I needed, always with help from other people. Getting involved has changed me. I am different now.'

(Beresford and Croft, 1993b, p. 1)

In Holland during the early 1970s Patients' Councils were set up in some psychiatric hospitals. This followed complaints by some service users about the quality of the mental health services. This user movement has grown so that all of Holland's psychiatric hospitals are required to have a patients' council. The hospital managements must consult with them regularly.

Similar structures of Patients' Councils have been set up in various hospitals in the UK. (Winn, 1990)

A ladder of empowerment

In this chapter two models of empowerment have been described. One emphasized empowerment as a consumer. The other emphasized greater control by users which we called the 'participatory' model. The real world is more complicated and it may be helpful to think in terms of a 'ladder' of degrees of empowerment. One example is shown in Figure 8.1:

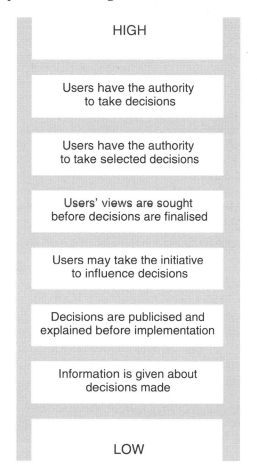

HIGH

Users have the authority
to take decisions

Users have the authority
to take selected decisions

Users' views are sought
before decisions are finalised

Users may take the initiative
to influence decisions

Decisions are publicised and
explained before implementation

Information is given about
decisions made

LOW

Figure 8.1: A ladder of empowerment.   (Hoyes et al, 1993, p. 9)

The various degrees of empowerment on the ladder depend on the amount of influence the user and carer have. In any particular organization, the ladder may help professionals to identify how participatory their organization actually is. By making current practice clearer and more explicit the ladder might help them to move towards a more participatory and empowering way of working.

Constraints on Empowerment

It would be a mistake to give the impression that empowerment is straight-forward and easy. In some respects there is less choice for users than before the 1990 NHS&CC Act. For example, people on income support now have considerably less power of choice over entering residential care than they had prior to April, 1993. Before April, 1993, they could choose that form of care and make the arrangements themselves. Now they have to go through a compli-cated assessment process with an uncertain outcome.

This section focuses on the topic of constraints to empowerment by giving particular attention to two areas:

1 The issue of resources and the view that there is not enough money to make community care work properly.
2 The issue of the lack of direct control by users of the finance to pay for their care and assistance. The Independent Living Fund was phased out in its original form, reducing considerably the possibility of users controlling their own care management.

Each of these constraints is now discussed in more detail.

Constraints on empowerment imposed by limited resources

It has been stressed that encouraging user-involvement does take time and commitment. Work in health and social care is a battleground of competing priorities and competing demands on resources. Councillors, officers, managers and practitioners have to live within their budgets and be concerned with obtaining value for money. One example of the dilemmas surrounding meeting need and facilitating choice within limited resources is given in the case study below concerning a real person, Mark Hazell:

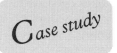

Mark Hazell

Mark Hazell, an adult with learning difficulties, refused Avon Social Services Department's offered placement, insisting on a more expensive one. He sought and was granted a judicial review of Avon County Council's decision not to place him in a residential home of his own choosing, Milton Heights in Oxfordshire. Avon Council wanted to place him in Berwick Lodge near Bristol, which cost almost £3000 a year less. This home was recommended in a joint report by a specialist social worker and the independent advocate, and the council maintained this cheaper option would satisfactorily meet Hazell's needs.

Two complaints panel hearings recommended Milton Heights for Hazell's needs, but Avon's social services committee rejected these recommendations.

At the judicial review in July, 1993 the judge ruled that Avon's assessment of Hazell should have taken into account his 'actual need' which included his psychological need to go to his chosen home. The review over-turned Avon's decision and ruled that Mark Hazell should be allowed to go to the home of his choice.

The situation of Mark Hazell is a good example of workers making decisions influenced by the budgetary pressures upon them. Choice as an aspect of empowerment may very often be limited by the resources that are available. Need will always outstrip resources and it seems likely that more situations coming to court will be one reflection of this.

In 1992 the Divisional Court ordered a judicial review of a case involving Hereford and Worcester County Council where the local authority had assessed a disabled person as needing a carer, but refused to supply one because it had a budget deficit. In the event the local authority settled out of court, and paid costs and compensation of nearly £8000, as well as providing the applicant with a carer.

The Hereford and Worcester case, as well as the situation of Mark Hazell, throw up the issue of what is done about 'need' which officers and councillors feel cannot be resourced from their budgets. As was mentioned in Chapter 5, in the early period of implementing community care, there was a lot of debate about whether need which could not be met should be recorded or not. The dilemma for local authorities was whether, if they recorded unmet need, they would experience more expensive challenges to their decisions through judicial reviews. At the time of writing, this still remains unresolved with social services departments varying considerably in their practice on the recording of need they know they cannot resource.

Health and welfare workers often feel very frustrated because they are being asked to deliver incompatible things. For example, they are being asked:

• to carry out a full assessment of needs;
• to be more responsive to 'consumers';
• to be gatekeepers of the public's money and limit spending;
• to ration limited resources;
• to act in an empowering way;
• to encourage participatory user-control.

Some of the pressures pull in different directions, so health and social care workers have to live with the contradictions. They have always been buffeted between competing pressures and competing values, often being in an ambiguous position. However, it may be that the contradictions and ambiguities feel greater with the NHS&CC Act. Take the social worker who is supposed to:

• act in an anti-oppressive way. This is given great emphasis by social work's training body, the Central Council for Education and Training in Social Work.
• do a financial assessment so that the user can make the appropriate contribution to the cost of the care.
• conduct user-led assessments. This is given great emphasis by the Government in its guidance on assessment and care management.
• work within severe budget constraints within a busy, pressurized office. This is the reality of social work over most of the country.

One problem with community care is that, although the guidance to the 1990

NHS&CC Act involves talk about 'choice' and 'user-led services', these concepts are really not built into the legislative framework. The Act and its guidance have raised expectations about community care provision and user-led assessments but the reality of limited resources and fixed budgets remains for the workers, officers and councillors.

Cradle to grave NHS?

Many people have associated the National Health Service with free health care for life. There used to be many more long-stay NHS beds where people would stay at no cost for many years and often until they died. These long-stay beds have been reducing quite quickly.

Previous guidance made it clear that no NHS patient should be transferred to a private nursing home against their wishes if they or their family then had to pay for the cost of that care. New draft guidance (August 1994) advises hospitals that patients who are in need of long-term care but short of specialist hospital treatment may be moved to private homes, with the bills paid for by social services departments or relatives. This moves them from the free NHS service to the means-tested Social Services. A big area of health care was redefined as social care – placing it within the means-testing system.

Lack of user-control over finance as a constraint on empowerment

Chapter 3 looked at the 'Independent Living Movement'. Independent living is very much about empowerment. Asking the question 'Does the legislation contribute to independent living?' may indicate the possibilities and problems of the legislation in relation to empowerment.

In this respect a study by Jenny Morris is helpful. The title of her study is 'Independent Lives'. In it she interviewed 50 disabled people. A central area of concern for Morris is whether community care policies can promote independent living for disabled people. Her answer to this will be presented below.

We have in the past tended to label and treat older and disabled people as 'dependent'. Our services have both created this dependence and reinforced it. For some physically disabled people one of the most empowering aspects of the late 1980s was the setting up of the Independent Living Fund. This gave disabled people control over their carers. Disabled people could become direct employers and control who did the caring and how it was done. The existence of the fund fed into the demands of the 'Independent Living Movement'.

We also saw in Chapter 3 how there is very little left of the Independent Living Fund in the 1990s. Moreover, local authorities are not supposed to make cash payments directly to users, but to purchase the services on their behalf.

> Morris argues that the philosophy of the Independent Living Movement is based on four assumptions:
> - that all human life is of value;
> - that anyone, whatever their impairment, is capable of exerting choices;
> - that people who are disabled by society's reaction to physical, intellectual and sensory impairment and to emotional distress have the right to assert control over their lives;
> - that disabled people have the right to fully participate in society.
>
> (Morris, 1993, p. 21)

The key issues of 'personal assistance' and 'Who is in control?' have been central to thinking about independent living. Morris argues that we see the need for personal assistance too readily as the need for 'care' and the need to be 'looked after'. Once the personal assistant is defined as a 'carer' who is 'looking after' then the very language indicates who is in charge and who has the power (Morris, 1993, p. 23).

Independent people (as in the Independent Living Movement) argue that they are in charge even if they do not do all the tasks themselves (for example, getting washed and dressed). This control over personal assistance rather than being controlled by personal assistance (however kind and well-meaning) is crucial. It is getting the service you want on your terms. For example,

- getting you up in the morning when you want;
- putting you to bed at night when you want;
- choosing what to eat and when;
- deciding yourself which tasks you want doing.

The physical inability to do certain tasks does not necessarily lead to dependency. What is important is the nature of the relationship with the person who is doing the tasks. This relates to who is in charge of what is done, how it is done and when it is done. Some of the lack of control which is commonly experienced is illustrated in the example in the following box:

An example of lack of control

William was one of the groups interviewed by Jenny Morris. Along with the others, he required some assistance in daily living tasks. He had experienced a range of negative attitudes held by both home carers and district nurses, all resulting from the fact that – at a meeting to which he was not invited – his mother informed social services and health authority managers that he is gay. William explained:

'It took me a while to work out what was going on. . . they were all so stand-offish but then one day, this woman just came out with a stream of incredible vitriolic abuse. And then it took me more time to work out that they think I've got AIDS – which I haven't.'

William feels very powerless because he is dependent on statutory services for personal assistance:

'I've tried talking to the home care organizer about the attitudes of her staff but she just denies it . . . she says they get training and they just have a job to do

> . . .but what can I do? I can't tell them not to come into my home, although I wish I could.'
>   William also described being handled very roughly:
>   'It's difficult to call it. . . well. . . abuse, really I suppose you would say. It's physical and verbal. It's just horrible, horrible. . . difficult to talk about. . . I put it out of me mind when it's not happening.'
>
> (Morris, 1993, p. 115)

Morris forcefully brings out that there is a conflict between an emphasis on informal care and supporting carers and the principles of independent living. She argues that, whilst some of the language of the community care changes appears as if it has been influenced by independent living ideas, this is not really the case:

> The aim of independent living, of full and equal participation in society, is held back by an ideology which does not recognize the civil rights of disabled people but instead considers them to be dependent people and in need of care.
>
> (Morris, 1993, p. 149)

In the interviews with 50 disabled people in her study Morris concludes that having the money to pay for personal assistance is the most important factor in enabling disabled people to have the kind of choices which non-disabled people take for granted.

The central issue here is who has the power and the choice as to which needs are met. Up to the mid-1990s, both the Department of Health and the Treasury continued to resist pressure to allow Social Services Departments to make direct payments to individuals.

A way forward for empowerment?

This chapter has looked at:

- government statements about encouraging empowerment;
- two models of empowerment – consumerist and participatory;
- constraints on empowerment posed by lack of resources and the lack of user-control over finance.

Social policy is full of contradictions and ambiguity. Health and social care workers have to work within this context. The community care changes present possibilities as well as constraints for user empowerment so we should return again to the possibilities. The box below shows some examples of good practice from a study of user empowerment in four local authorities.

Examples of good practice of user involvement:

- supporting users with learning difficulties on planning groups;
- purchasing advocacy services;
- funding transport for people to attend user group meetings;
- enabling HIV service users to switch to an alternative home care provider;
- piloting 'cash for care' through an Independent Living scheme.

(Hoyes et al., 1993, p. 44)

Checklist on how workers can empower service users

In 1992 the trade union COHSE (now part of UNISON) and MIND published *Guidelines for Empowering Users of Mental Health Services*. Within it there is a useful checklist addressed directly to workers, on how they can empower service users who are mentally distressed. The checklist is as follows:

'Staff work within constraints imposed by their employers. But within these constraints there are choices. Depending on the choices you make, service users will feel you are on their side, indifferent or against them. You can contribute towards our recovery or our hopelessness.

Here we propose some do's and don'ts for staff wanting to relate to individual service users in ways which are empowering.

1 **DO** let us know what our rights are. Often we feel we have none. Let us know about our rights to refuse treatment, leave, make a complaint, or be represented at a mental health tribunal. It helps to be told more than once, and to also be given the information in writing.

2 **DON'T** hide behind a mask of professionalism. Don't use words we don't understand. Don't pretend you know more than you do. Mental health work is full of uncertainty, confusion, controversy and contradictions. Honesty is empowering.

3 **DO** ask us what we want. You may not be able to provide it. You may disagree. But do ask us. Potentially at least, we are the experts on our own needs.

4 **DON'T** dismiss our complaints and worries as symptoms of our "mental illness". Too often people's physical illnesses have been disregarded, women sexually molested in hospitals and hostels have not been believed, and genuine grievances have not been taken seriously.

5 **DO** recognize our talents, capabilities and potential. Support us in trying new activities, taking on responsibilities and finding outlets for our creativity.

6 **DON'T** panic when we express feelings. Often it is useful to sob, shout, scream, shake or shiver. We appreciate being listened to and encouraged. We want space to do that without disturbing other people.

7 **DO** tell us as much as you can about the drugs we are on, the diagnosis we have and the options open to us.

8 **DON'T** write us off. We are fed up with being told 'You will have to take these pills for the rest of your life,' or 'There's no cure for manic depression.'

Throwaway negative or dismissive remarks may cause great hurt and be a source of pain to us for years. Many of us have overcome the most disabling distress, often despite the pessimistic predictions of so-called experts.

9 **DO** talk to us. Emotional distress is isolating. Help us break through it. Be friendly and treat us as equals. But don't try to force us to talk when we clearly don't want to.

10 **DON'T** forget that we live in a multicultural society, in which people have different beliefs and values. Learn all you can about the people who use your service, not least by asking them.'

(Read and Wallcraft, 1992, p. 15)

Some possibilities

Earlier in the chapter material and ideas were drawn from Morris' study, *Independent Lives*. In spite of her dissatisfaction with aspects of the community care arrangements, she argues that things can be done within the changes to ensure that the new community care policies promote the human and civil rights of disabled people. A summary of these views is given below.

Changing attitudes

Most of us care for others at some point in our lives, whether paid or unpaid. Can we try to think how the other person's control over their own life can be promoted? Our own attitudes and behaviour need to change so that we are promoting control and choice rather than diminishing it.

Assessing need

Disabled people are entitled to full, comprehensive assessments under the 1990 legislation. These assessments should be led by the needs of the person and not by the services which happen to be available. This requires the assessor to develop an ethic which assesses according to need and not to succumb to pressure to assess according to resources. Disabled people should be as involved as possible in the assessment process and in determining the operation of the care plan.

Care management

The policy guidance says that it might be possible for some service users to play a more active part in their own care management. This is not independent living but nevertheless there is a possibility here of shifting the emphasis of control from the provider to the user.

Organizations of disabled people

Local authorities and health authorities can encourage and facilitate the development of organizations controlled by disabled people themselves.

Direct payments

Local authorities are not allowed to make direct payments to users for them to buy their own services. However there does seem to be some scope for payments to be made either through trust funds or voluntary organizations.

Morris' final plea is:

> The ideology of caring which is at the heart of current community care policies can only result in institutionalization within the community unless politicians and professionals understand and identify with the philosophy and aims of the Independent Living Movement.
>
> (Morris, 1993, p. 179)

*A*ctivity

If you are a health or social care worker, you should know which user-groups are available locally. People who you work with may wish to make contact with them. Draw up a list of the user-groups which are available locally. In relation to mentally distressed people, the local branch of MIND should be able to help, as should some workers who work with mentally distressed people. (In 1988 MIND started its Consumer Network, MINDLINK and the networks newsletter, *MINDWAVES*, is an important channel of communication.)

In any area there are usually a number of local groups, some of which are linked into national networks. Try to find out if there are any self-advocacy groups of people with learning disability or any other user-groups of disabled people.

Carers as a group have become increasingly organized and you could find out what carers groups exist in your area. As a national coordinating network of many carers groups, the Carers National Association should be able to provide you with details of any groups in your area.

*A*ctivity

If you are a carer, either paid or unpaid, the ideas of user empowerment and of the independent living movement may represent a challenge to your thinking and to your practice as a carer. Try to think through and discuss with others the ways in which the ideas might alter your practice.

Key questions

1 In what way can information help to empower?
2 Outline two models of user empowerment.
3 In what ways have the early 1990s community care changes encouraged or discouraged user empowerment?
4 Suggest some ways in which user empowerment can be taken forward by health care and social care workers.

Further reading

Winn, L. *Power to the People*, King's Fund Centre, London, 1993.
Croft, S. and Beresford, P. *Getting Involved: A Practical Manual*, Open Services Project, London, 1993.

Beresford, P. and Croft, S. *Citizen Involvement,* Macmillan, London, 1993. Suzy Croft and Peter Beresford have written a great deal about user-involvement.

Read, J. and Wallcraft, J. *Guidelines for Empowering Users of Mental Health Services,* COHSE and MIND. A history of the self-advocacy movement for mental health users and practical guidelines on user empowerment.

Fiedler, B. and Twitchin, D. *Achieving User Participation*, King's Fund, London, 1992. A product of the Living Options in Practice Project. (The Project has been working with eight localities since January, 1990 to establish systems for user participation for people with severe physical and sensory disabilities.)

Jenny Morris' book, *Independent Lives,* has been drawn on in this chapter and her ideas could be followed up by a study of this book.

References

Amin, K. (1992) *Poverty in Black and White*, London: Child Poverty Action Group.

ARC and NAPSAC (1993) *It Could Never Happen Here*, Chesterfield: ARC and NAPSAC.

Atkin, K. and Rollins, J. (1993) *Community Care in a Multi-Racial Britain: A Critical Review of the Literature*, London: HMSO.

Atkin, K. (1992) Similarities and Differences Between Informal Carers, in Twigg, J. (1992) *Carers: Research and Practice*, London: HMSO.

Audit Commission (1986) *Making a Reality of Community Care*, London: HMSO.

Barnes, M. (1993) 'Building Change and Making It Stick: A Local Authority Wide Perspective', in Beresford, P. and Harding, T. (1993) *A Challenge To Change*, London: NISW.

Baxter, C., Poona, K., Ward, L. and Nadirshaw, Z. (1990) *Double Discrimination*, London: King's Fund Centre and Commission for Racial Equality.

Begum, N., Hill, M. and Stevens, A. (1994) *Reflections*, London: CCETSW.

Beresford, P. and Croft, S. (1993) *Citizen Involvement*, London: Macmillan.

Beresford, P. and Harding, T. (1993) *A Challenge To Change*, London: NISW.

Blakemore, K. and Boneham, M. (1994) *Age, Race and Ethnicity*, Buckingham: Open University Press.

Bornat, J. *et al.* (1993) *Community Care: A Reader*, London: Macmillan.

Brown, H. and Smith, H. (1992) *Normalization*, London: Routledge.

Cameron, E., Badger, F. and Evers, H. (1989) 'District Nursing, the Disabled and the Elderly: Who Are the Black Patients?' in *Journal of Advanced Nursing*, vol. 14, pp. 376–82.

CCETSW (1991) *Disability Issues*, London: CCETSW.

Challis, D. and Davies, B. (1986) *Case Management in Community Care*, London: Gower.

Croft, S. and Beresford, P. (1993) *Getting Involved: A Practical Manual*, London: Open Services Project.

Dalley, G. (1988) *Ideologies of Caring*, London: Macmillan.

DHSS (1981) *Growing Older*, London: HMSO.

DoH (1989a) *Working for Patients*, London: HMSO.

DoH (1989b) *Caring for People*, London: HMSO.

DoH (1990a) *Community Care in the Next Decade and Beyond: Policy Guidance*, London: HMSO.

DoH (1990b) *Guidance on Standards for Residential Homes for Elderly People*, London: HMSO

DoH (1990c) *Developing Services for Disabled People*, London: DoH.

DoH (1991a) *Care Management and Assessment: Practitioners' Guide*, London: HMSO.

DoH (1991b) *Care Management and Assessment: Managers' Guide*, London: HMSO.

DoH (1991c) *Implementing Community Care: Purchaser, Commissioner and Provider Roles*, London: HMSO.

DoH (1991d) *Purchase of Service: Practice Guidance*, London: HMSO.

DoH (1991e) *The Right To Complain: Practice Guidance on Complaints Procedures in Social Services Departments*, London: HMSO.

DoH (1992a) *The Health of The Nation*, London: HMSO.

DoH (1992b) *Committed to Quality*, London: HMSO.

DoH (1993a) *Mental Illness: Key Area Handbook*, London: DoH.

DoH (1993b) *HIV/AIDS and Sexual Health: Key Area Handbook*, London: DoH.

DoH (1993c) *No Longer Afraid: Practice Guidelines*, London: HMSO.

DoH (1993d) *Managing the New NHS*, London: DoH.

Family Policy Studies Centre (1991) *The Family Today: Fact Sheet 1*, London: FPSC.

Fiedler, B. and Twitchin, D. (1992) *Achieving User Participation*, London: King's Fund.

Goffman, E. (1968) *Asylums*, England: Penguin.

Graham, H. (1993) 'Feminist Perspectives on Caring', in Bornat, J. *et al.* (1993) *Community Care: A Reader*, London: Macmillan.

Green, H. (1988) *Informal Carers*, London: HMSO.

Griffiths, R. (1988) *Community Care: Agenda for Action*, London: HMSO.

Gunaratnam, Y. (1993) *Checklist: Health and Race*, London: King's Fund Centre.

Harris, V. (1994) *Review of the report of the Inquiry into the care and treatment of Christopher Clunis: A Black Perspective*, London: Race Equality Unit.

Harrison, K. (1994) 'Nobody's Business', in *Community Care Magazine*, 24 March, 1994.

Harvey, M. and Tisdall (1992) *Vocational Qualifications in Care*, Birmingham: Pepar.

Harrison, L. and Means, R. (1993) Brokerage in Action, in Smith, R. *et al.* (1993) *Working Better Together for Community Care*, Bristol: School for Advanced Urban Studies.

HMSO (1993) *Social Welfare*, London: HMSO.

Holman, B. (1993) *A New Deal for Social Welfare*, Oxford: Lion Publishing.

House of Commons Social Services Committee (1985) *Second Report 1984–85, Community Care With Special Reference To Adult Mentally Ill and Mentally Handicapped People*, London: HMSO.

House of Commons Social Services Committee (1990) *Community Care, Fifth Report: Carers*, London: HMSO.

House of Commons Health Committee (1993) *Sixth Report, Community Care, The Way Forward*, London: HMSO.

Hoyes, L., Jeffers, S., Lart, R., Means, R. and Taylor, M. (1993) *User Empowerment and the Reform of Community Care*, Bristol: School for Advanced Urban Studies.

Hunter, D.J. (1988) *Bridging the Gap*, London: King Edward's Hospital Fund for London.

Jackson, P.W. (1990) *Britain's Deaf Heritage*, Edinburgh: Pentland Press.

King's Fund Centre (1991) *Meeting the Challenge*, London: King Edward's Hospital Fund.

Law Commission (1993) *Mentally Incapacitated and Other Vulnerable Adults: Public Law Protection*, London: HMSO.

Leat, D. (1993) *The Development of Community Care by the Independent Sector*, London: PSI.

LGDF (Local Government Drugs Forum) (1993) *Fast Track Assessment for People With Alcohol and Drug Problems*, London: LGDF.

Manning, N. and Page, R. (1992) *Social Policy Review*, Canterbury: Social Policy Association.

Meredith, B. (1993) *The Community Care Handbook*, London: Age Concern.

MIND (1993) *Policy on Black and Minority Ethnic People and Mental Health*, London: MIND.

Morris, J. (1991) *Pride Against Prejudice*, London: The Women's Press.

Morris, J. (1993) *Independent Lives*, London: Macmillan.

North, C., Ritchie, J., and Ward, K. (1993) *Factors Influencing the Implementation of the Care Programme Approach*, London: HMSO.

Oliver, M. (1990) *The Politics of Disablement*, London: Macmillan.

Parker, G. (1992) 'Counting Care: Numbers and Types of Informal Carers', in Twigg, J. (1992) *Carers: Research and Practice*, London: HMSO.

Patel, N. (1990) *A 'Race' Against Time*, London: Runnymede Trust.

Phaure, S. (1991) *Who Really Cares?* London: London Voluntary Service Council.

Pritchard, J. (1992) *The Abuse of Elderly People: A Handbook for Professionals*, London: Jessica Kingsley.

Read, J. and Wallcraft, J. (1993) *Guidelines for Empowering Users of Mental Health Services*, London: COHSE and MIND.

Read, J. and Wallcroft, J. (1994) *Guidelines on Advocacy for Mental Health Workers*, London: UNISON and MIND.

Renshaw, J. (1988) 'Care in the community: individual care planning and case management', in *British Journal of Social Work*, Supplement, No. 18.

Ritchie, J., Dick, D. and Lingham, R. (1994) *The Report of the Inquiry into the Care and Treatment of Christopher Clunis*, London: HMSO.

Royal College of Nursing (1994) *An Inspector Calls?* London: RCN.

Simpson, F. (1991) 'Carers at the Crossroads', in *Contact Magazine (Summer)*. London: Radar.

Skellington, R. (1992) *Race in Britain Today*, London: Sage.

Srivos, S. (1992) 'The Limits to Integration', in Brown, H. and Smith, H. (1992) *Normalization*, London: Routledge.

Stevens, A. (1993) *Back from the Wellhouse*, London: CCETSW.

Survivors Speak Out (1988) *Self-Advocacy Action Pack*, London: SSO.

Torkington, P. (1991) *Black Health: A Political Issue*, London: Catholic Association for Racial Justice.

Townsend, P. (1979) *Poverty in the United Kingdom*, London: Penguin.

Twigg, J. (1992) *Carers: Research and Practice*, London: HMSO.

Utting, W. (1994) *Creating Community Care*, London: Mental Health Foundation.

Vousden, M. (1987) *Nye Bevan Would Turn in His Grave*, Nursing Times, 83(32), pp. 18–19.

Watson, M. (1993) *Implementing Community Care*, London: NISW.

Webb, R. and Tossell, D. (1991) *Social Issues for Carers*, London: Edward Arnold.

Williams, A. (1992) *Caring for People . . . Caring for Profit*, London: London Voluntary Service Council.

Williams, F. (1992) 'Somewhere over the Rainbow: Universality and Diversity in Social Policy', in Manning, N. and Page, R. (1992) *Social Policy Review*, Canterbury: Social Policy Association.

Williams, P.C. (1993) 'Care Management and Assessment With Blind and Partially Sighted People', in Stevens, A. (1993) *Back from the Wellhouse*, London: CCETSW.

Wilson, M. (1993) *Mental Health and Britain's Black Communities*, London: King's Fund Centre.

Winn, L. (1990) *Power To the People*, London: King's Fund Centre.

Useful Addresses

The following list gives the addresses of organisations mentioned in this book.

Age Concern England
Astral House
1268 London Road
London
SW16 4EJ

Alzheimer's Disease Society
Gordon House
10 Grencoat Place
London
SW1P 1PH

**British Council of Organisations
of Disabled People**
De Dradelei House
Chapel Street
Belper
Derbyshire
DE56 1AR

British Deaf Association
38 Victoria Place
Carlisle
Cumbria
CA1 1HU

Carers National Association
20/25 Glasshouse Yard
London
EC1A 4JS

Child Poverty Action Group
1–5 Bath Street
London
EC1V 9PY

Commission for Racial Equality
Elliot House
10/12 Allington Street
London
SW1E 5EH

Crossroads
10 Regent Place
Rugby
Warwickshire
CV21 2PN

**Derbyshire Centre for Integrated
Living**
Long Close
Ripley
Derbyshire
DE5 3HY

Disability Alliance
Universal House
88–94 Wentworth Street
London
E1 7SA

Health Education Authority
Hamilton House
Mabledon Place
London
WC1H 9TX

King's Fund
126 Albert Street
London
NW1 7NF

Livings Options in Practice Project
126 Albert Street
London
NW1 7NF

MENCAP
123 Golden Lane
London
EC1Y ORT

Mental Health Foundation
37 Mortimer Street
London
W1N 7RJ

MIND
15/19 Broadway
Stratford
London
E15 4BQ

Open Services Project
Tempo House
15 Falcon Road
London
SW11 2PJ

People First
Instrument House
207–215 Kings Cross Road
London
WC1X 9DB

Policy Studies Institute
100 Park Village East
London
NW1 3SR

Race Equality Unit
5 Tavistock Place
London
WC1H 9SN

Survivors Speak Out
34 Osnaburgh Street
London
NW1 3ND

The Terence Higgins Trust
52/54 Gray's Inn Road
London
WC1 8JU

Index